PRACT

Other Titles of Interest

PRACTICAL ELECTRONIC FILTERS

by

Owen Bishop

BERNARD BABANI (publishing) LTD
THE GRAMPIANS
SHEPHERDS BUSH ROAD
LONDON W6 7NF
ENGLAND

Please Note

Although every care has been taken with the production of this book to ensure that any projects, designs, modifications and/or programs, etc., contained herewith, operate in a correct and safe manner and also that any components specified are normally available in Great Britain, the Publishers do not accept responsibility in any way for the failure, including fault in design, of any project, design, modification or program to work correctly or to cause damage to any other equipment that it may be connected to or used in conjunction with, or in respect of any other damage or injury that may be so caused, nor do the Publishers accept responsibility in any way for the failure to obtain specified components.

Notice is also given that if equipment that is still under warranty is modified in any way or used or connected with home-built equipment then that warranty may be void.

First Published – November 1991
Reprinted – April 1997

British Library Cataloguing in Publication Data
Bishop, O. N. (Owen Neville), *1927–*.
Practical electronic filters.
I. Title
621.3815324

ISBN 0 85934 244 1

Printed and bound in Great Britain by Cox & Wyman Ltd, Reading

Warning

Certain circuits and projects included in this book involve mains voltages and wiring. These are not recommended for beginners or those with little knowledge or experience of working with mains wiring and voltages.

About This Book

Although most books on filters are extremely mathematical — for filters are some of the most mathematically-linked of all electronic circuits — this book deals with filters in a non-mathematical way. It reviews the main types of filter, explaining how each works and what it is used for. Most chapters end with one or more practical projects to illustrate the topics covered in that chapter.

To help the reader select a suitable project, they are graded in three levels:

Level 1 projects are suitable for beginners, who have a little experience of building projects from kits or from magazine articles. Some books that outline constructional methods are listed in Appendix A.

Level 2 projects are of average standard. After building one or two Level 1 projects, a beginner should be able to tackle some of those at Level 2.

Level 3 projects are more advanced in that their circuits are more elaborate. It is not so much that they are difficult to build as that, if the constructor has made a mistake or fault in their construction, it is more difficult to diagnose what is wrong.

The descriptions of each project include a circuit diagram and a description of how the project works. The components required are specified in the diagram or in a special component list. Except where high-precision (1% or 2%) resistors are essential for the filters, all resistors can be the commonly-used ¼W carbon or metal film resistors with 5% tolerance. However, it is preferable to use the 0.6W metal film resistors with 1% tolerance, which are available at low cost from some suppliers. Precision capacitors may be required in certain projects, as explained later.

The circuit diagrams of each project show the pin-out of all transistors used as seen from below. They show the pin numbers for most ICs. An exception is made in the case of those logic ICs which include a number of identical gates. With these, it does not matter which gate is used in a given part of the circuit. Often the constructor will prefer to use one rather than another, so as to simplify the layout or wiring of the circuit board. The gate inputs and outputs of these ICs have been left un-numbered in the circuit diagrams. Appendix B gives the pin-out of these ICs.

There is scope for modifying and experimenting with several of the projects by incorporating one or more of a range of filter circuits. When designing these filters, refer to the last chapter, Chapter 11, which summarises the main types of filter, with practical design details. This chapter will be of use also when building filter-based projects other than those in this book.

Owen Bishop

Contents

Chapter 1

INTRODUCING SIGNALS AND FILTERS

This book is about electronic filters — what they are, how they work, and why they are used. Mathematics has been largely avoided and, since the book is aimed at the practical reader, most chapters end with one or two constructional projects. These will help you to understand more about filters and their uses.

A filter is a circuit which alters the characteristics of a periodic electronic signal. A periodic signal is one which varies regularly in time. Often the signal is a varying voltage, such as that shown in Figure 1. The *period* of a signal is the length of

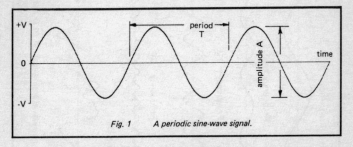

Fig. 1   A periodic sine-wave signal.

time over which the form of the signal is repeated. The number of periods in one second is known as the *frequency*. The amount by which the voltage swings to either side of its central value is its *amplitude*.

The signal shown in Figure 1 is one of the simplest, known as a *sine wave*. It has this name because the voltage changes in the same way as the sine of an increasing angle changes. Given the amplitude A and the frequency f (or the period T), and using a table of sines or the sine function on a pocket calculator, it is an easy matter to plot a graph of any sine wave. Figure 1 is the result of plotting a sine wave using a computer and printer.

More often in practical circuits the signal consists not of just a pure sine wave but of a mixture of sine waves of different

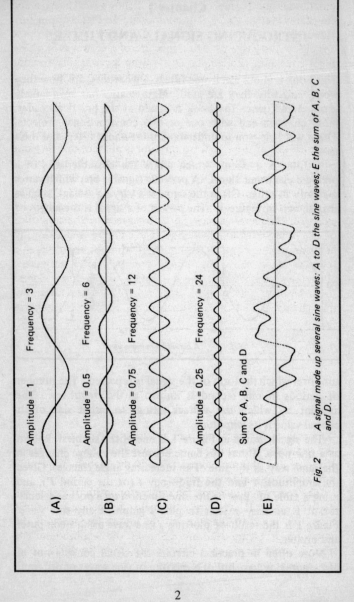

Fig. 2   A signal made up several sine waves: A to D the sine waves; E the sum of A, B, C and D.

amplitudes and frequencies. Figure 2 shows such a signal and the sine waves of which it is composed. In fact, we can turn this statement the other way around and say that all periodic signals can be analysed into a mixture of sine waves of differing frequencies and amplitudes. Even such angular-looking waveforms as sawtooth, triangular, and square waves can be considered to be sine wave mixtures.

Types of Filter

When a periodic signal is passed through a filter circuit, the composition of the sine-wave mixture is altered. As the name 'filter' implies, a filter can not add anything to the mixture. It can only remove or partly remove sine waves of particular frequencies. There are several categories of filter, depending on what they do to the mixture. A *low pass* filter, for example, completely removes or at least reduces the amplitude of the sine waves of high frequency. Figure 3 shows what happens to the signal of Figure 2(E) when passed through a low-pass filter which has filtered out the highest frequency altogether, and reduced the amplitude of the next highest frequency by a little more than half. The two lower frequencies are passed through unchanged. Note that the overall

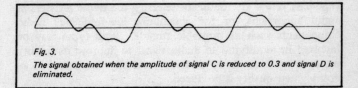

Fig. 3.
The signal obtained when the amplitude of signal C is reduced to 0.3 and signal D is eliminated.

amplitude of the signal has been reduced owing to the removal and reduction of some of its components. But the biggest effect is that the most rapid (that is the highest-frequency) twists and turns no longer appear.

The action of a *high-pass* filter is the opposite to that of the low-pass filter. It passes only the higher frequencies. Figure 4 shows the result of filtering out the lowest frequency of the waveform of Figure 2(E) and reducing the amplitude of the second lowest frequency. Now the long-term 'swell' has gone, leaving only the short-period waves.

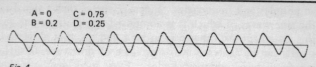

A = 0   C = 0.75
B = 0.2 D = 0.25

Fig. 4.
The signal obtained when the amplitude of signal B is reduced to 0.2 and signal A is eliminated.

By combining low-pass and high-pass filters in the same circuit we arrive at *band-pass* filters. These pass frequencies within a given range but remove or reduce the lower and the higher frequencies. The converse of a band-pass filter is a *notch filter* which removes or reduces frequencies in a given narrow range but passes both lower and higher frequencies.

Low-pass filters have many applications in electronic circuits. In the audio field they may be used for emphasising low-frequency signals in the bass register, or for reducing high-frequency components of the signal, for example, tape hiss. In medical research they may be used to pick out low-frequency signals such as those originating from the brain from a confusing hotchpotch of other signals. They are often used in other applications to eliminate unwanted high-frequency oscillations. High-pass filters are useful for selecting the treble registers in audio equipment, or for eliminating low-frequency audio components such as turntable rumble. Both types may be involved in modifying an audio signal to improve its fidelity or, as in synthesisers, to alter it so radically that sound of an entirely new quality is produced.

One of the most common uses of band-pass filters is in the tuning circuits of radio and TV sets. Here the transmission from one particular station is passed through the filter, while transmissions from stations operating on other radio-frequencies are filtered out. Band-pass filters are also important in oscillators of many types, passing the required frequency through to the amplification stage and removing all other frequencies. The reverse situation occurs when we wish to remove a particular frequency, say the 50 Hz 'mains hum', from an audio signal, for which purpose a notch filter may be employed.

4

In this book we deal in detail with filters of all the above types. The projects at the end of each chapter provide further practical examples of the ways in which the filters are used.

Passive and Active Filters
The most elementary types of filter are constructed from resistors, capacitors and, sometimes, inductors. These are known as *passive filters* since they merely dissipate part of the power of the incoming signal, and pass the remainder. The advent of cheap, easily used, operational amplifiers has given scope for the design of filters which draw additional power from an external source and can actively work on the incoming signal. They can even incorporate amplification of the signal so that, although the signal has been filtered to remove unwanted frequencies, its amplitude is as great as or greater than that of the unfiltered signal. Such filters are called *active filters*. As we shall explain in Chapter 4, active filters have many advantages over the passive types, including the fact that they do not need inductors.

Digital Filters
Filtering is a matter of transforming a complex input waveform into a usually less complex output waveform. The transformation, like any mathematical transformation, is defined by a set of equations. Although few equations appear in this book, they nevertheless exist and determine exactly what happens during filtering. In the filters referred to above we use a combination of resistors, capacitors, inductors (sometimes) operational amplifiers (often) to perform the mathematical operations required. Such circuits are, in effect, analogue computers, dedicated to one particular transformation.

It is also possible to transform a signal by using a digital computer. An analogue-to-digital converter is used to turn the varying signal voltage into a series of numbers. These represent the voltage as converted at regular intervals of time. We now use a computer to perform various mathematical operations which have the effect of filtering out certain frequencies. This has to be done rapidly; usually the computer is operating in real time. The mathematically processed signal is then turned back into analogue form using a digital-to-analogue converter.

Filtering by mathematically transforming the digitised signal is known as *digital filtering*. Digital filters can be programmed to perform all the functions of analogue filters and also, since there are almost limitless possibilities in the computations, to produce effects that are difficult to obtain by straightforward analogue filters.

Chapter 2

RESISTORS, CAPACITORS AND FREQUENCY

Resistors and capacitors are to be found in all filter circuits, so a study of the way these components behave is of importance to an understanding of filters. Inductors too, are occasionally used in filters, though less often nowadays, so we shall deal with these only briefly. Operational amplifiers replace inductors to a large extent, and their properties are dealt with in Chapter 4.

As its name implies, a resistor acts to resist the flow of an electric current. When a p.d. is applied across a resistor, a current flows through it. The size of current is determined by the size of p.d. which is causing it to flow and the value of resistance which is opposing its flow. There is a very simple relationship between the p.d. V, the current I and the resistance R :

$$V = IR$$

where V is in volts, I is in amps and R is in ohms. This is an expression of the relationship known as *Ohm's Law*. If the p.d. is varying, for example if the resistor is connected across the terminals of a microphone or the output of an audio amplifier, the current varies in exactly the same way, instant by instant. Thus, in Figure 5, the graph which shows how p.d. V varies with time has exactly the same form as the graph of how the current I varies with time. The relative amplitude of each signal depends on the value of the resistor.

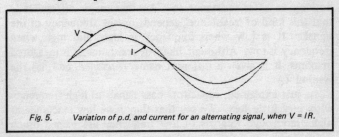

Fig. 5.   Variation of p.d. and current for an alternating signal, when $V = IR$.

Currents and Capacitors

With a capacitor, the relationship between p.d. and current is rather more complicated. Resistance has no part to play in this because the two plates of a capacitor are separated by a layer of insulating material, the *dielectric*. Thus no current can actually flow through a capacitor from one plate to the other. However, one particular property of capacitors leads to an interesting effect. This property is the tendency of a capacitor to hold the p.d. between its plates at a constant value. If the potential of one plate is made to rise or to fall, there is a tendency for the potential of the other plate to rise and fall by the same amount.

If a *rapidly* alternating current flows toward and away from one plate of a capacitor, the potential of that plate rises and falls rapidly. But the p.d. between the plates remains more-or-less unchanged. As a result, the potential of the other plate rises and falls rapidly too and by approximately the same amounts. The result is a rapidly alternating current (of the same size and frequency) flowing away from and toward the other plate. The overall effect is as if the alternating current had flowed across the capacitor. By contrast, if a *slowly* alternating signal is applied to one plate of a capacitor, there is time for the p.d. between the plates to increase and decrease. As the potential of one plate rises and falls slowly, the p.d. slowly increases and decreases. The potential of the other plate remains more-or-less constant. Relatively little current flows away from it or toward it. Since little current flows on that side of the capacitor, the capacitor is behaving as if it has 'resistance'. This 'resistance' is quite different from the resistance of a resistor. For one thing there is no actual flow of current through the capacitor, so there is nothing to offer resistance to. Another major difference is that this kind of 'resistance' depends on the frequency of the signal. It is low when frequency is high, and high when frequency is low. Although, like true resistance, it is measured in ohms, it is given a different name, *reactance*, and has the symbol X_C.

As just explained, capacitors pass signals of high frequency with very little loss. We say that they have low reactance at high frequency. Signals of low frequency are passed much less easily – reactance is high at low frequencies. To sum up, the reactance of a capacitor is inversely related to frequency.

There is one more factor that influences reactance, and that is capacitance. If capacitance is small, a given current flowing into the capacitor brings about a relatively large change of potential. On the other hand, if capacitance is high, the same current has a relatively small effect. For a given alternating signal, the changes in potential produced in a small capacitor are greater than those produced in a large capacitor. As explained above, reactance is the result of changes in potential and so is inversely related to capacitance. The reactance of a capacitor is determined by just two factors, frequency and capacitance, and is inversely related to each of them. This relationship is expressed in the equation:

$$X_C = 1/2\pi f C.$$

When referring to the reactance of a capacitor we must always quote the frequency.

Phase Changes

Two alternating signals may have the same shape (for example they may both be pure sine waves) but they may differ in *amplitude* and in *frequency*. Even if they are of the same frequency they may differ in *phase*. In Figure 6(a) the two signals have the same frequency, but differ in amplitude. They are in phase, by which we mean that each signal reaches the same point in its cycle at exactly the same time. They are exactly 'in step'. For example, they both pass through zero going from negative to positive at exactly the same moment. In Figure 6(b) the same pair of signals are out of phase. They are 'out of step'. Signal B *lags* behind signal A by a constant amount at every stage of its cycle. Alternatively we can say that signal A *leads* signal B.

Phase lag or lead is expressed as an angle, the *phase angle*, which has the symbol ϕ measured in degrees or radians. The length of one complete cycle is taken to be 360° or its equivalent, 2π radians. In Figure 6(b) the signal B lags signal A by 34°, or 0.6 radians. We use this concept of phase angle to analyse what happens when an alternating signal is applied to

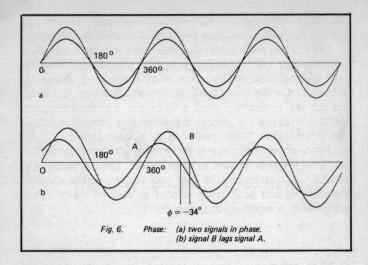

Fig. 6.   Phase: (a) two signals in phase.
                     (b) signal B lags signal A.

a circuit containing a capacitor.

In Figure 7 an alternating signal is applied to a resistor and capacitor connected in series. Since they are in series, the same current I flows through the resistor and *apparently* flows through the capacitor. The p.d. V_R across the resistor at any instant is given by the equation previously quoted:

$$V_R = IR$$

The p.d. across the capacitor is calculated by a similar equation in which reactance replaces resistance:

$$V_C = IX_C .$$

At any instant the total p.d. V_T across the resistor and capacitor is the sum of V_R and V_C. Figure 8 shows how these quantities vary in time during three cycles of a sine wave. V_R varies in direct proportion to I, as would be expected from the equation above. They are in phase and, to keep the diagram simple, we have used the same curve to represent both quantities. Assume that the capacitor begins (at time t_0) by being charged in the negative direction, so V_C is negative. The

10

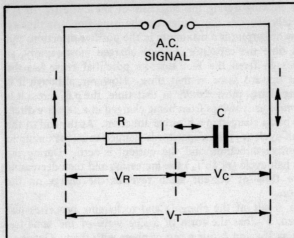

Fig. 7.   Voltages across a resistor and a capacitor in series.

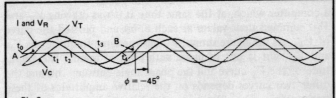

Fig. 8.

The voltages of Fig. 7, when V_R and V_C have equal amplitude. The distance A to B or t_0 to t_4 represents a phase angle of $360°$.

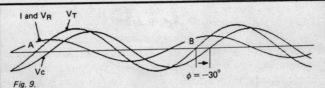

Fig. 9.

The voltages of Fig. 7 at low frequency. The distance A to B represents a phase angle of $360°$.

11

current flowing during the first half of the cycle (t_0 to t_2) completely reverses the charge on the capacitor. At time t_1 the flow of current is a maximum in the positive direction, and at that time the capacitor is being charged most rapidly, as can be seen from the fact that its potential curve has the steepest upward slope at that time. However, although it is receiving charge most *rapidly* at that time, the p.d. across it is a *minimum* as it swings from being charged in a negative direction to being charged in a positive direction. At the end of the first half-cycle (t_2) the capacitor is charged to its maximum in the positive direction, and the current is zero. During the second half-cycle (t_2 to t_4) the increasing and then decreasing negative flow of current again reverses the charge on the capacitor.

As a result of the charging and recharging processes just described, V_C has the form of a sine wave of the same frequency as V_R and I, but is out of phase with them. Owing to the nature of the charging process, the phase difference is $90°$, with the V_C lagging behind I and V_R.

During each cycle the total p.d. V_T is the sum of the two out-of-phase sine waves. The curves in Figure 8 were drawn by a computer which, at the same time as it was drawing V_R and V_C, summed their values at each point and plotted the curve of V_T. As the figure shows, V_T has the same frequency as V_R and V_C, but is out of phase with both of them. The amplitude of the V_T curve and the phase angle between this and the other two curves depends on the relative amplitudes of these two curves. The relative amplitudes are determined by the values of R, C and the *frequency of the signal.* This is illustrated by Figures 8 to 10. In Figure 8, the signal frequency is such that the resistance of the resistor is exactly equal to the reactance of the capacitor:

$$R = X_C = 1/2\pi f C$$

and thus the frequency is:

$$f = 1/2\pi RC.$$

The result of this is that V_R and V_C have equal amplitude. V_T has an amplitude rather greater than either of them. It is never twice as great, since V_R and V_C are out of phase and therefore not at both their maxima at the same times. In fact, V_T has an amplitude 1.4 times as great as V_R (and V_C). Also, V_C lags 45° behind V_T. We say that $\phi = -45°$. These relationships apply whenever R and X_C are equal.

In Figure 9 we see what happens with the same resistor and capacitor when the signal frequency is lower. The curve for V_R is as before, but that for V_C has greater amplitude as the capacitor has greater reactance at the lower frequency. The resultant curve for V_T shows it once again to have a larger amplitude than V_R or V_C, but now the phase angle has decreased to −30°.

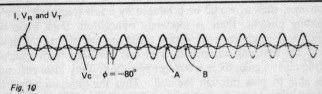

Fig. 10

The voltages of Fig. 7 at high frequency. The distance A to B represents a phase angle of 360°.

Figure 10 shows the result of increasing the frequency, with the same resistor and capacitor. Now V_C has a very small amplitude and has little effect when added to V_R. The curve of V_T follows so closely to that of V_R, that they do not appear as separate curves on the plot. The amplitude of V_T is only slightly greater than that of V_R. The phase lag of V_C is now increased to −80°.

We return to the amplitude and phase relationships of V_R, V_C and V_T in the next chapter.

Inductors

An inductor is a coil of insulated wire which is generally wound on a core, former or armature made of electromagnetic material. The core is usually of soft iron or a ferroceramic material such as Ferrite. In several ways an inductor is the opposite of a capacitor. For instance, there is a

13

continuous conduction path through its coil. The coil may have a resistance of only a few ohms, sometimes only a fraction of an ohm. It offers negligible resistance to the passage of a steady electric current. But the operative word in the previous sentence is 'steady', meaning *direct current*. When the current is an alternating one, electromagnetic effects come into play.

When current flows through a coil a magnetic field is generated. It is a property of such coils that there is opposition to anything that would tend to change the intensity and direction of that magnetic field. The more rapid the change that is attempted, the more strongly is that change opposed. With *no* change there is no opposition, which is why a steady current can flow freely through the coil. With a moderate change, such as would be produced by a low-frequency alternating current, there is moderate opposition. Such a signal passes through the coil, with a small amount of loss. With a rapidly changing current, such as that resulting from a high-frequency signal, there is strong opposition. Very little current is able to pass through the coil. Thus the inductor offers a varying 'resistance' to the flow of alternating signal currents. As with the capacitor, this is not true resistance for we have said that the coil has extremely low resistance. This 'resistance' is known as inductive reactance, and is given the symbol X_L to distinguish it from capacitive reactance X_C. It depends on two factors, one of which is the self-inductance L of the coil. This is determined by the number of turns in the coil and its physical dimensions. The other factor is frequency and the two may be combined together in the equation:

$$X_L = 2\pi f L.$$

This expresses the fact that inductive reactance increases with increasing frequency, the opposite behaviour to capacitive reactance. Given that inductors have frequency-dependent reactance, it is plain that they can be used in a similar way to capacitors, except that the circuits operate in the reverse manner. Filters can certainly be built with inductors but there are disadvantages. One is that inductors tend to be large, heavy

14

and costly. Another disadvantage is that it is not easy to make an inductor with an accurately specified self-inductance. They also have the annoying property of picking up interference from any electromagnetic fields in the neighbourhood. Finally, it is so much easier, cheaper and more precise to replace the inductor with a circuit based on an operational amplifier. About the only remaining use for inductors in filtering is when we wind a few turns of wire around a ferromagnetic ring, or thread the wire through ferromagnetic beads to filter out radio-frequency signals.

Chapter 3

PASSIVE FILTERS

Passive filters are built solely from passive components such as resistors, capacitors and inductors.

Before explaining how passive filters work, let us look at a very commonly used sub-circuit, the *potential divider* (Fig. 11). A current I flows from the positive input terminal, through resistor A, then through resistor B and to the negative line. We are assuming for the moment that there is no other circuit connected to the output terminals, so that *all* the current flowing through A also flows through B.

Since the current is the same throughout, the p.d. across each resistor is proportional to their resistances, as is the p.d.

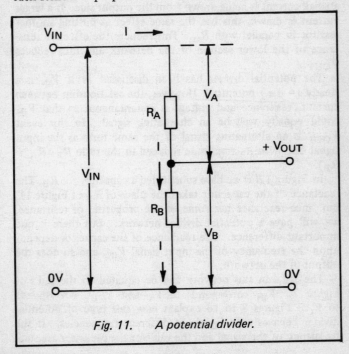

Fig. 11.   A potential divider.

V_{IN} across the two resistors in series. The output p.d. of this sub-circuit (or *network*, as it is more often called) is V_B which we will from now on refer to as V_{OUT}. Since p.d.s are proportional to resistances, we can write:

$$\frac{V_{OUT}}{V_{IN}} = \frac{R_B}{R_A + R_B}$$

which gives the result:

$$V_{OUT} = V_{IN} \times \frac{R_B}{R_A + R_B} .$$

This equation holds true provided that no current or only a small current is being drawn from the output side. If a larger current is drawn, this has the same effect as putting another resistor in parallel with R_B. This reduces the effective resistance of the lower section of the network and thus reduces V_{OUT}.

The potential divider has been discussed as if V_{IN} is a steady (= d.c.) potential. However, the relationship between current, resistance and voltage is instantaneous so that V_{IN} could equally well be an alternating signal. In this event V_{OUT} is an alternating signal of the same form as the input signal but with its amplitude reduced in the ratio $R_B/(R_A + R_B)$.

In Figure 12(a) we have substituted a capacitor for R_B. The reactance of the capacitor takes the place of R_B of Figure 11, but since reactance has some of the properties of resistance, we still have a potential divider network. But there is one important difference. The reactance of the capacitor depends upon the frequency of the input signal V_{IN}, and so does the output of the network.

The p.d.s in this network can be equated to the p.d.s of Figure 7. V_{IN} corresponds to V_T and V_{OUT} corresponds to V_C. Figures 8 to 10 explain how this type of potential divider behaves with signals of different frequencies. If the frequency of the signal and the value of the capacitor are such

18

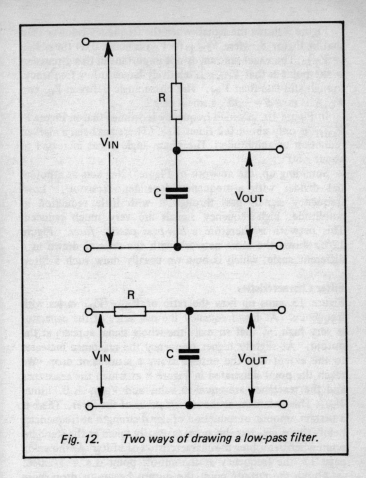

Fig. 12. Two ways of drawing a low-pass filter.

that $X_C = R$, we have the situation shown in Figure 8. In Figure 8, the amplitude of V_T is approximately 1.4 times V_C so, in Figure 12(a) the amplitude of V_{OUT} (i.e. V_C) is approximately $1/1.4$ times that of V_{IN} (i.e. V_T). Converting this to decimals we find that V_{OUT} is approximately 0.7 times V_{IN}. In addition, it lags behind V_{IN} by 45°. We say that $\phi = -45°$. This is a situation that we shall return to again shortly.

19

Figure 9 shows the signals when the frequency is lower than that in Figure 8. Here V_{OUT} (= V_C) is about 0.84 times V_{IN} (= V_T). The exact amount is not important in this discussion — the point is that V_{OUT} is relatively larger at low frequency, though still less than V_{IN}. The phase angle between V_{IN} and V_{OUT} is now $\phi = -30°$, a smaller lag.

In Figure 10, in which frequency is 5 times that in Figure 8, V_{OUT} is only about 0.2 times V_{IN}. There has been a marked reduction in amplitude. The phase angle ϕ has increased to about $-80°$.

Summing up, the network of Figure 12(a) acts as a potential divider with a frequency dependent 'resistor'. Low-frequency signals pass through it with little reduction in amplitude; high-frequency signals are very much reduced. This network is therefore a *low-pass passive filter*. Figure 12(b) shows the same network with the resistor drawn at a different angle, which is how we usually draw such a filter.

Filter Characteristics

Figure 13 sums up how the ratio of V_{OUT}/V_{IN} varies with frequency. At low frequency the reactance of the capacitor is very high, so that virtually the whole signal appears at the output. At slightly higher frequency the reactance increases to the extent that the output shows a significant drop. We reach the point illustrated in Figure 8 at which the resistance and the reactance are equal in value and V_{OUT} is 0.7 times V_{IN}. This is known as the *cut-off point* of the filter. There is a certain amount of reduction of signal strength at frequencies below this point, but this point is usually taken as the standard point when describing the characteristics of a filter. As shown on page 12, the frequency at the cut-off point is $f = 1/2\pi RC$.

Above the cut-off point the output begins to drop more sharply. It assumes a steady downward gradient. At even higher frequencies the reactance is so high that virtually nothing of the signal remains.

To understand this graph fully we have to know what is meant by the term *decibel*, symbol dB. The decibel is a way of expressing the *ratio* between two quantities. Here we use it to express the ratio of V_{OUT} to V_{IN}. The ratio is calculated like this:

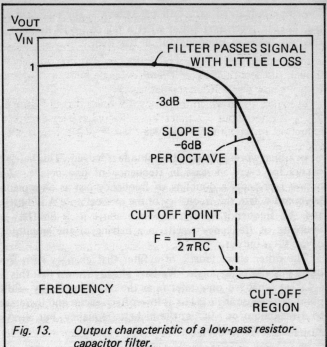

Fig. 13.   Output characteristic of a low-pass resistor-capacitor filter.

$$n = 20 \times \log_{10}(V_{OUT}/V_{IN}).$$

We use ' n ' as the subject of this equation to indicate that since we begin the calculation with a ratio, the result is a pure number. Decibels are not *quantities* such as volts, amps and ohms — they represent a *ratio* calculated in a particular way.

In Figure 8, the ratio V_{OUT}/V_{IN} is 0.7. Expressed in decibels, this becomes:

$$n = 20 \times \log_{10} 0.7 = 20 \times -0.1549 = -3dB.$$

The cut-off point is sometimes referred to as the 'minus 3 decibel' point.

The steady downward fall in response above the cut-off point can also be described in terms of decibels. In Figure 13 the slope is marked as '−6dB per octave'. The equation on page 21, in reverse, specifies what a fall of −6dB means. If the ratio between input and output is a, then:

$$-6 = 20 \log_{10} a$$

$$\log_{10} a = -20/6 = -0.3$$

$$a = \text{antilog}_{10} \, -0.3 = 0.5$$

In other words, the signal amplitude is halved. This halving occurs for every increase in frequency of one octave. An octave represents a doubling of frequency just as on a piano keyboard where the frequency of the musical note A is 440Hz and the frequency of A′, an octave above it, is 880Hz. A doubling of frequency results in a halving of the amplitude of the filter output.

The other characteristic of a filter that changes with frequency is the phase angle. We have already shown that this is −45° at what we now refer to as the cut-off point or −3dB point. The phase angle is less at lower frequencies and increases to a maximum of −90° at the highest frequency, but always V_{OUT} lags behind V_{IN}.

High-pass Filter
If the resistor and capacitor of Figure 12(a) are exchanged, we obtain a potential-divider network (Fig. 14) in which the output signal appears across the resistor. In terms of Figure 8, V_{IN} is equivalent to V_T (the same as in the low-pass filter) but V_{OUT} is now equivalent to V_R. As might be expected, the action of this network is the opposite of the low-pass filter. At the frequency when the R and X_C are equal, the V_{OUT} is 0.7 times V_{IN} (remember that in Figure 8, $V_R = V_C$). In other words, this is the −3dB cut-off point. It occurs at the same frequency for both low-pass and high-pass filters.

Figure 15 shows that above the cut-off point the output increases a little until there is virtually no loss. The low-frequency section of the curve rises at +6dB per octave.

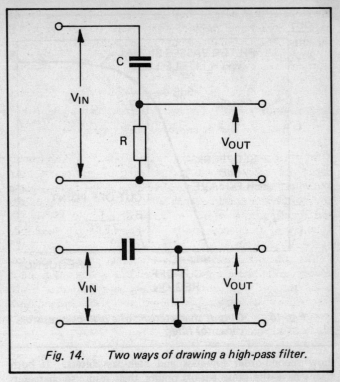

Fig. 14. *Two ways of drawing a high-pass filter.*

The effect of a high-pass filter on phase angle is the opposite to that of a low-pass filter. In such a filter the output is V_R. At the cut-off point, V_{OUT} *leads* V_{IN} by $+45°$ as before. At lower frequencies the lead *increases* to a maximum of $+90°$. At higher frequencies it is less than $+45°$.

Orders

The two filters described above each consist of a single stage. We refer to these as *first-order* filters. Sometimes we wish to build a filter with a sharper cut-off, to obtain a characteristic curve with a slope greater than $-6dB$ or $+6dB$ per octave. One way of doing this is to use the output of one filter as the input of a second filter. This produces a two-stage filter, usually known as a *second-order* filter. Figures 16 and 17 respectively

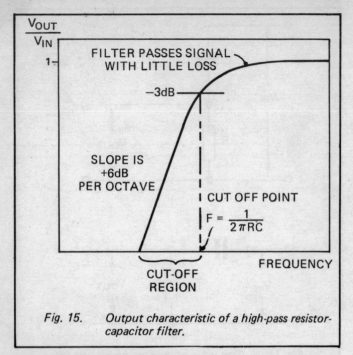

$\dfrac{V_{OUT}}{V_{IN}}$

1—

FILTER PASSES SIGNAL
WITH LITTLE LOSS

—3dB—

SLOPE IS
+6dB
PER OCTAVE

CUT OFF POINT

$F = \dfrac{1}{2\pi RC}$

FREQUENCY

CUT-OFF
REGION

*Fig. 15.   Output characteristic of a high-pass resistor-
capacitor filter.*

show second-order low-pass and high-pass filters. If both stages have the same cut-off points, their response characteristics are identical. In a first-order low-pass filter, the slope of the curve is —6dB per octave in the cut-off region. A second low-pass filter placed after this increases the slope of the curve by a further —6dB, giving a total reduction of —12dB per octave. This corresponds to reducing the input amplitude by a quarter per octave.

Adding a second stage to a filter also increases the phase angle. For example with two identical stages, each with $\phi = -50°$, the second-order filter has a total phase lag of 100°. Since the maximum lag of a single stage is almost 90°, the maximum lag of a second-order filter is 180°. In this case the input and output signals are of completely opposite phase. This has an important bearing on filters used in certain types of oscillator circuits.

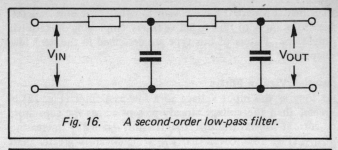

Fig. 16.   A second-order low-pass filter.

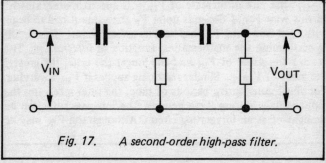

Fig. 17.   A second-order high-pass filter.

Filters need not end at the second order. It is permissible to add even more stages, with a corresponding increase in the sharpness of cut-off. However when we add stages to a filter, even just adding the second stage of a second-order filter, we have to take into account the effect each succeeding stage has on the operation of the previous stages. As mentioned on page 18, the equations describing the action of a potential divider rely on there being no loss of current at the output. Although loss of current can be minimised, it can not be prevented altogether. For this reason the cascading of stages does not necessarily produce a filter that behaves exactly as the 'sum' of its parts. Although cascading many stages may give a very steep slope to the curve in the cut-off region it has little effect in sharpening the 'knee' of the curve around the cut-off point. If requirements are relatively uncritical a second order filter constructed solely of resistors and capacitors may be acceptable. For filters of higher order a much better response is obtained by using inductors as well. As explained on page 14 these lead to other problems and the best solution is to turn to active filters, employing operational amplifiers. Filters of this type are described in the next few chapters.

Another View of Filters

As long as the input voltage to a low-pass filter (Fig. 12) is greater than the voltage already present across the capacitor, a current flows through the resistor, gradually increasing V_{OUT} (Fig. 18). Given that V_{IN} is significantly greater than V_{OUT}, the rate of increase of V_{OUT} is approximately steady. In this way V_{OUT} depends upon V_0 the value it had to begin with, and how long V_{IN} has held its present value. The circuit is performing the mathematical function of *integration*. The greater the value of V_{IN} and the longer the time, the greater the value of V_{OUT}. Similar reasoning applies if V_{IN} is varying. For short consecutive periods of time, the filter integrates the input voltage during these periods. The low-pass filter can be thought of as an integrating circuit. Although the V_{IN} may be

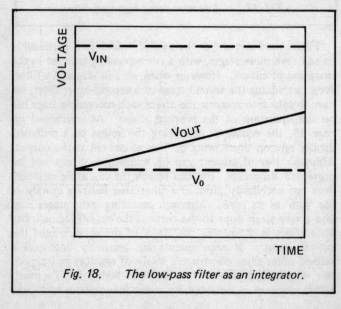

Fig. 18.   The low-pass filter as an integrator.

26

fluctuating widely, V_{OUT} shows only long-term changes.

Returning to the concept of filtering, the circuit is passing only the low-frequency components of the input signal. The circuit of Project 1 at the end of this chapter is an example that makes this function clear.

The converse applies to high-pass filters. In Figure 14, a sudden (i.e. high-frequency) increase of V_{IN} results in a more-or-less equal increase in the voltage on the other plate of the capacitor. Before the next such pulse arrives, there is time for the excess charge to leak away through the resistor. V_{OUT} shows a short spike, as in Figure 19. The height of the spike depends on the rate at which V_{IN} increases. In other words, V_{OUT} depends upon the *rate of change* of V_{IN}. The filter is performing the mathematical operation of *differentiation.*

Figure 20 shows the effect of a high-pass filter when the input is a square wave. There is an upward spike coinciding with the beginning of each pulse and a downward spike at the end of each pulse (i.e. as V_{IN} changes in a negative direction).

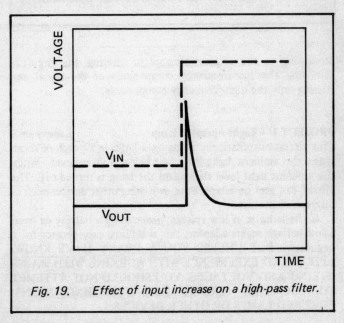

Fig. 19.   Effect of input increase on a high-pass filter.

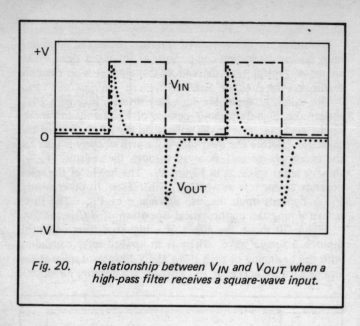

Fig. 20. *Relationship between V_{IN} and V_{OUT} when a high-pass filter receives a square-wave input.*

Returning to the original concept of filtering, the circuit is removing the low-frequency components of the signal and passing only the high-frequency components.

PROJECT 1 – Light-operated lamp   *Level 1 or 3*

This circuit automatically turns on a lamp in a porch or room when the ambient light level falls below a given level. When the ambient light level rises again the lamp is turned off. The circuit can also be adapted for switching other devices such as buzzers, or motors.

If the lamp is of low voltage, powered by a battery or from a low-voltage mains adaptor, this is a fairly easy project for a beginner. BUT UNLESS YOU ALREADY HAVE KNOWLEDGE AND EXPERIENCE WITH WORKING WITH MAINS WIRING AND VOLTAGES, YOU SHOULD NOT ATTEMPT TO USE THIS CIRCUIT FOR SWITCHING MAINS-POWERED LAMPS OR OTHER DEVICES.

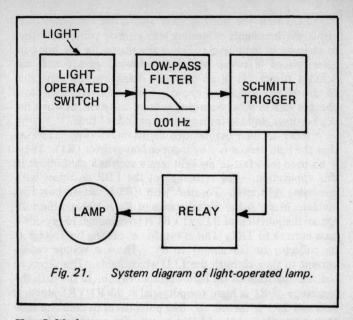

Fig. 21.   System diagram of light-operated lamp.

How It Works

This is an example of the use of a filter to prevent unwanted signals from triggering the system. The system diagram (Fig. 21) shows that a light-operated switch circuit is used to detect the level of ambient light. The sensor is placed where it will be affected by daylight but unaffected by the lamp when it is on. The output voltage of the switch circuit rises with increasing light intensity. When the voltage exceeds a given level, the Schmitt trigger circuit operates the relay which turns the lamp on.

One of the problems with a circuit which depends upon light level is that of differentiating between the slow changes of level occurring at dusk and dawn, or by occasional excessive cloud, and the more rapid changes caused by other means. Rapid changes may occur when small clouds pass across the sun. If the area is partly shaded by trees, the moving shadows of leaves being blown by the wind may bring about very rapid changes in the amount of light reaching the sensor. The shadows of persons or vehicles passing by, particularly when the sun is near the horizon, may also affect the sensor. At night, the headlights of passing vehicles may continually lead to changes in light level. This is the reason for the low-pass filter placed between the light-operated switch and the Schmitt trigger. It filters out rapid changes in the signal due to the effects described above. Conversely, it passes slow changes such as those occurring at dawn and dusk, or when the sky becomes clouded for significant periods of time.

A more detailed examination of the circuit (Fig. 22) shows that the light sensor is a light-dependent resistor (R1). There is no need for a fast-acting light sensor such as a photodiode in this application. The resistance of the LDR decreases with increasing light level. Together with VR1 it forms a potential divider. In the light, the resistance of R1 is low and the voltage at the junction of R1 and VR1 is high enough to provide a base current to TR1. This is turned on, causing the voltage at its collector to fall almost to 0V. The low voltage causes current to flow through the LED which lights. This serves to indicate the state of the light-operated switch. In the dark the resistance of R1 is high, the potential at the R1/VR1 junction falls and TR1 is turned off. The potential at its collector rises almost to +6V and the LED goes out. The exact light level at which the changeover between 'light' and 'dark' states occurs is set by adjusting VR1.

The effect of alternate light and dark periods is to produce an alternating signal at the collector of TR1. The low-pass filter consists of R5, R6, C1 and C2. The −3dB point for this filter is 0.01Hz, equivalent to a period of oscillation of 100 seconds. The output of the filter rises or falls appreciably only when the input signal is high or low for periods of several seconds. This eliminates short-lived effects such as those mentioned earlier.

The final part of the circuit, the Schmitt trigger, is intended to produce a sharp switching action. If the light level is low for long enough, the filter output rises very slowly. As it rises past a given level, a little over 3V, the trigger circuit changes state suddenly, de-energising the relay coil. The relay contacts are wired so that they make contact, turning on the lamp. Then if the light level is high for long enough, the filter output falls slowly. Owing to the nature of the trigger circuit, it does

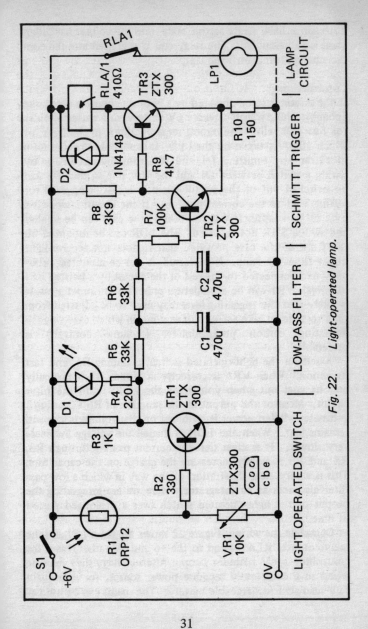

Fig. 22. Light-operated lamp.

31

not change back to its former state until the voltage has fallen some way below 3V. The relay coil is energised and the contacts break, turning off the lamp.

Construction
If the circuit is to be powered by a battery, choose a case large enough to hold a high-capacity 6V battery, or a battery-holder for four 'D' cells. The circuit requires 20mA in the light, of which 10mA is taken by the LED. It is possible to economise in current by omitting D1 and R4 from the circuit, or by wiring a switch between D1 and the +6V line so that D1 can be switched out of the circuit when it is not being used for setting VR1 to the correct position. If the circuit is powered by a mains adaptor (6V d.c., 300mA) the case can be smaller and switch S1 is not required. The LDR can be mounted on the front of the case provided that it does not receive light direct from the lamp. If preferred, it can be mounted externally and connected to the rest of the circuit by a twisted pair of wires. VR1 can be a miniature preset potentiometer but it is likely that the triggering level may need to be adjusted from time to time to take account of seasons, in which case a panel-mounting carbon potentiometer ('volume control') is preferable.

Assemble the light-operated switch, including D1, and test its action. When VR1 is correctly adjusted, D1 is normally on but goes out when you shade the LDR. Add the filter circuit. Monitor the output at the junction of R6/C2, using a voltmeter. When power is switched on, the voltage is low and remains low. When the LDR is shaded the voltage increases very slowly. It is clear that the current passing through R3, R5 and R6 is slowly increasing the charge on the capacitors. This is a very clear illustration of the way in which a low-pass filter also acts as an integrator. Here we are integrating the output of the light-operated switch over a prolonged period of time.

Complete the wiring. Figure 22 shows the lamp LP1 and the relay contacts RLA1 wired to the +6 and 0V rails. This is for controlling a 6V filament lamp. Alternatively, they may be wired to a completely separate power source, for example a 12V lead-acid rechargeable battery. The mains can be used as a power source, provided that the relay contacts are rated to withstand mains voltages and currents. If the mains is used great care must be taken that there is no possibility of any connection between the relay contact circuit and the other parts of the circuit. You should attempt this only if you have had previous experience with wiring such circuits.

The correct setting for VR1 is established at a time when the ambient light is at the level at which switching is to occur. Turn VR1 so that the LED is glowing at approximately half its maximum brightness.

Special Components

Resistors
R1   ORP12 or similar light-dependent resistor
            (= cadmium sulphide cell)

Semiconductors
D1   light emitting diode
D2   1N4148 silicon signal diode
TR1–TR3 ZTX300 npn transistor (3 off)

Miscellaneous
RLA/1 for low-voltage operation, this can be a miniature or sub-miniature pcb mounting relay; for mains operation a larger type is required with contacts suitably rated. In either case the coil is rated at 6V and it has single *change-over* contacts.

Chapter 4

LOW-PASS ACTIVE FILTERS

Chapter 3 showed that although a passive filter is easy to build, it has two serious disadvantages. One is that V_{OUT} is necessarily less than V_{IN}. The loss in signal strength is considerable in a high-order filter consisting of many stages. The second disadvantage is illustrated in Figure 13, in which it is seen that the response curve is broadly rounded in the region around the cut-off frequency. This means that it is not possible to retain a signal of a given frequency while making a useful reduction in a signal of a closely neighbouring frequency. While increasing the order of the filter makes the cut-off curve steeper for frequencies much higher than the cut-off point it has very little effect in the region of cut-off itself. In other words, we need to give the curve a sharper 'knee'.

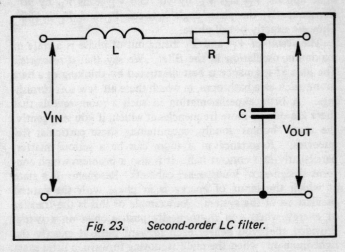

Fig. 23. Second-order LC filter.

One way of improving the shape of the curve is to include an inductor in the filter. Figure 23 shows one type of second-order LC low-pass filter. This has *two* components which are reactive, the inductor and the capacitor. At low frequencies the inductor has low reactance, passing the signal readily to the low-pass filter consisting of R and C. The capacitor has high reactance at low frequencies so the signal passes on with little or no reduction in strength. At high frequencies the inductor has high reactance, reducing signal strength which is further reduced by the RC combination, owing to the low reactance of the capacitor. The overall effect is a low-frequency pass-band and a −12dB per octave fall in the cut-off region.

A more important effect is what happens around the −3dB point. At that point the reactance of the inductor equals that of the capacitor. As can be seen in Figure 8, for an RC filter at the frequency at which $R = X_C$, the waveform of V_C, the alternating voltage across the capacitor lags behind the V_R waveform by 90°. In a filter consisting of an *inductor* and a resistor, at the frequency at which $R = X_L$, the converse applies. The voltage V_L across the inductor *leads* V_R by 90°. If the filter has an inductor, a resistor and a capacitor, as in Figure 23, and the frequency is such that $R = X_C = X_L$, the same applies; V_C lags V_R by 90° and V_L leads V_R by 90°. Consequently, the phase angle between V_C and V_L is 180°. They are exactly out of phase.

The result of V_C and V_L being out of phase is a state of maximum oscillation in the filter. We say that it *resonates.* The idea of resonance is best illustrated by thinking of a bare room, such as a bathroom, in which there are few soft furnishings. A little experimentation in such a room reveals that there are one or more frequencies at which, if you sing gently, the room 'booms' loudly, accentuating these particular frequencies. Resonance in a room can be a serious matter, particularly in a concert hall. It is also a problem which concerns designers of loudspeaker cabinets. Resonance is a state at which the input of energy is in phase with the natural oscillations of the system. An example of this is the transfer of energy when you rhythmically push a child on a swing. Provided that you deliver each forward push at exactly the right moment, when the child is moving forward, a little extra energy is transferred to the child at each oscillation. The amplitude gradually builds up. If you deliver the pushes at the

36

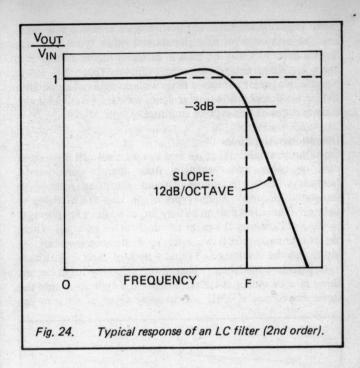

Fig. 24.   Typical response of an LC filter (2nd order).

wrong frequency, you are eventually pushing the child forward when the swing is moving backward, and the amplitude decreases.

In an LRC filter at its −3dB frequency, the input signal is delivering energy to the filter at its natural rate of oscillation. Consequently voltage swings increase in amplitude. As V_C increases, V_L decreases, and vice versa. Thus the swing of V_C is not opposed but rather is enhanced by the swings in V_L. Thus V_C, which is also the output voltage of the filter, has its maximum amplitude.   The result is shown in Figure 24, in which there is a peak of output around the resonant frequency. This peak 'sharpens' the knee of the curve around the cut-off frequency.   Given certain combinations of R, X_C and X_L the peak may be even higher, so that the filter shows overall gain around the cut-off frequency.

37

An inductor improves the performance of a low-pass filter and the same applies to high-pass and other types of filter. Several inductors may be used in filters of higher orders. But there are disadvantages in using inductors (page 14) so, if possible, we prefer to replace them with operational amplifiers. Before we describe how this is done, we need to examine the main features of this type of amplifier.

Operational Amplifiers

Operational amplifiers, or *op amps* as we shall call them from now on, were built originally from discrete components. Nowadays they are almost without exception realized as integrated circuits. Many types of op amp are available as two or four identical amplifiers in a single I.C. package.

Figure 25 shows the main terminals of an op amp. There are two inputs, which we refer to as the non-inverting (+) input and the inverting (−) input. Both of these inputs have a very high impedance. That is to say, very little current flows into or out of these terminals. In a typical op amp the input impedance is 2MΩ and in some types of op amp the

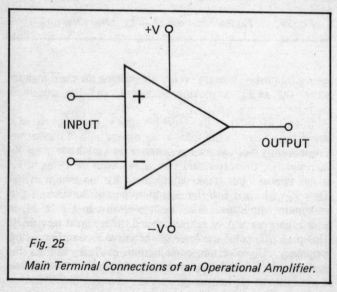

Fig. 25

Main Terminal Connections of an Operational Amplifier.

input impedance may be as high as $10^{12}\,\Omega$, or 1 teraohm, so that the current flowing can be totally ignored. The difference between the two inputs is described later.

There is a single output terminal which, in contrast with the input terminals, has very low impedance, typically $75\,\Omega$. It can supply a relatively large output current without a significant drop in the output voltage.

Finally, there are the two power supply terminals. Usually an op amp is operated on a dual power supply. The ground rail is taken as the reference voltage, 0V. The power rails have voltages equally above and below the ground rail. For example, if the power supply is ±6V, the +V terminal is at +6V and the −V terminal is at −6V.

Op amps often have two additional terminals for balancing the circuit, particularly for correcting for errors in the amplifier which make it behave as if there is a small difference between the input voltages when in fact there is not. In the applications described in this book, such errors are too small to be important so we are not concerned with how to correct them.

Returning to the input terminals, we see from Figure 25 that they have opposite polarity. The relationship between input and output is as follows, assuming that voltages more positive than +V or more negative than −V are not allowed:

Input conditions	*Resulting output**
Both inputs at the same voltage	Zero volts
(+) input at higher voltage than (−)	Positive
(+) input at lower voltage than (−)	Negative

*Output voltage always referenced to the 0V line.

The size of the output voltage, whether positive or negative, depends on the *difference* between the voltages at the two inputs, so the op amp is a *differential amplifier*. Further it has very high gain (200,000 or more) so that a very small difference in voltage is often sufficient to make the output swing as far as it can toward +V or −V. This gain is referred to as the *open loop* gain. Note that there is an upper limit to the rate at which the output of an op amp can change. This is known as the *slew rate*. This varies from one type of op amp to another. If the slew rate is low, the output is not able to respond fully to rapidly alternating input signals. As a result the effective gain of the amplifier falls off at higher frequencies. In most amplifiers the output voltage can swing to within a volt or so of the supply rails, but no further. In a few types the output can swing almost to +V and −V. No amplifiers are able to produce an output beyond the range +V to −V.

With the features described above, the op amp is a versatile device that can be used in a variety of ways. Here we consider only two ways in which it is commonly used in filter circuits. The first of these is the *non-inverting amplifier*. This is an amplifier in which the output is greater than the input and has the same polarity. Figure 26 shows that the circuit

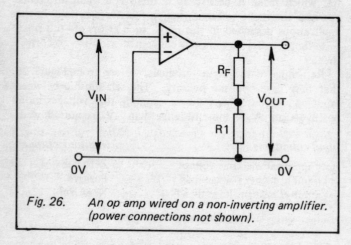

Fig. 26.   An op amp wired on a non-inverting amplifier. (power connections not shown).

involves *feedback*. Furthermore, since the feedback goes to the (−) input terminal, it is *negative feedback*. This type of feedback limits the gain and causes the circuit to have overall stability of operation.

In Figure 26 the feedback resistor R_F and resistor R1 act as a potential divider. If the potential at the junction of R_F and R1 is v then:

$$v = V_{OUT} \times \frac{R1}{R_F + R1}$$

The voltage v is fed back to the (−) input. If V_{IN} increases a very little above v, so that the difference between V_{IN} and v is just enough to produce the output V_{OUT}, the circuit reaches a stable state in which:

$$V_{OUT} = A \times (V_{IN} - v)$$

where A is the open loop gain of the amplifier.

This gives:

$$\frac{V_{OUT}}{A} = V_{IN} - v .$$

But A is very large compared with V_{OUT} so that the expression on the left of the equation approximates to zero and thus:

$$V_{IN} - v = 0$$

or

$$v = V_{IN} .$$

In words, the circuit becomes stable when the voltages at the input terminals are almost equal. They are not *exactly* equal as this would make V_{OUT} become zero. The small difference between them (amplified by 200,000 times or more) is just enough to give the required output voltage.

Substituting V_{IN} for v in the first equation we find:

$$V_{IN} = V_{OUT} \times \frac{R1}{R_F + R1}$$

or

$$V_{OUT} = V_{IN} \times \frac{R_F + R1}{R1} .$$

The gain of the amplifier *circuit* (as opposed to the huge open loop gain of the op amp IC) is thus $(R_F + R1)/R1$.

For example, if $R_F = 100\text{k}\Omega$ and R1 = 10kΩ, the gain is
(100k + 10k)/10k = 11 . Note that the gain of the circuit is
determined only by the values of the resistors, not by the
performance of the op amp IC. If high-precision resistors are
used the gain is set with great precision.

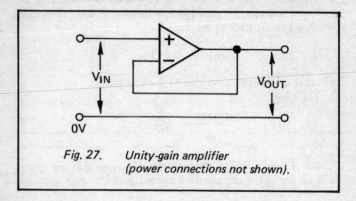

*Fig. 27.   Unity-gain amplifier
(power connections not shown).*

One special case of the non-inverting amplifier is illustrated
in Figure 27. In this the whole output voltage is fed back to
the (–) input. Thus $v = V_{OUT}$ and the circuit becomes stable
when $V_{OUT} = V_{IN}$. The gain is 1. This circuit is sometimes
known as a *voltage follower*. Although the circuit produces no
gain, it has the property that it requires only a very small
input current, yet can supply a relatively large output current.
This is a very useful property for matching impedances, that
is to say, for providing ample current where it is needed.

The other important circuit configuration for an op amp is
the *inverting amplifier* (Fig. 28). This too has negative feedback and so, as before, V_{OUT} is such that the input voltages
are almost equal. In this circuit the (+) input is held at 0V,
so (–) will be very close to 0V too. Figure 29 explains what
happens. Given a positive input voltage V_{IN} a current I flows
toward the (–) terminal which is at 0V. Ohm's Law tells us
that $I = V_{IN}/\text{R1}$. This current does not enter the input
terminal, which has very high impedance, but carries on
through the feedback resistor and enters the output terminal.
An equal current I flows through the feedback resistor and so

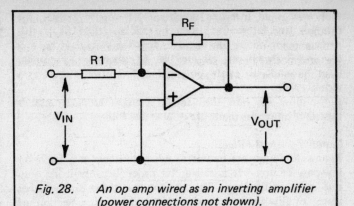

Fig. 28. *An op amp wired as an inverting amplifier (power connections not shown).*

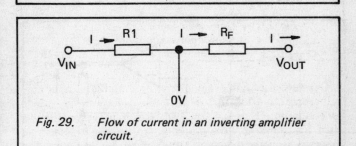

Fig. 29. *Flow of current in an inverting amplifier circuit.*

the value of V_{OUT} must be such as to cause that current to flow: $I = -V_{OUT}/R_F$. The minus sign indicates that here I is flowing *away from* the (−) terminal. Since it is the same I in both resistors we find:

$$\frac{V_{IN}}{R1} = -\frac{V_{OUT}}{R_F}$$

giving

$$V_{OUT} = -\frac{V_{IN} \times R_F}{R1}.$$

The gain of this circuit is $-R_F/R1$. The negative sign shows

43

that this is an inverting amplifier. If $R_F = 100k\Omega$, for example, and R1 = 10kΩ, then the gain is $-100k/10k = -10$.

One point about this circuit is that the voltage at the (−) terminal is always very close to 0V. In effect the (−) terminal is at 'ground' or 'earth' potential and is often known as a *virtual earth*.

We now see how the various types of amplifier circuit described above are made use of in active filters.

Simple Low-pass Filter
Figure 30 shows the circuit of what is known as a 1st order low-pass section. It is called '1st order' because it has only one stage of filtering. This implies that there can be other stages of filtering to follow it. It could be just a 'section' of a much more elaborate filter circuit.

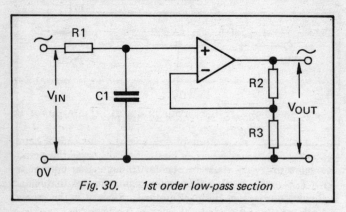

Fig. 30.   1st order low-pass section

Comparing Figure 30 with Figures 12(b) and 26, it is clear that this is simply an ordinary RC passive filter followed by a non-inverting amplifier. R1 and C1 determine the cut-off frequency, while R2 and R3 set the amount of amplification. As far as filtering goes, it inherently has the same properties as the RC passive filter. The improvements are:

(1) The output from the RC stage is amplified to restore or enhance the output voltage.

(2) The low output impedance of the amplifier means that a larger current can be drawn from the output without over-

44

loading the filter section and degrading its performance.

VCVS Filters
The name of these filters is derived from the fact that we use the op amp as a *voltage-controlled voltage source.*

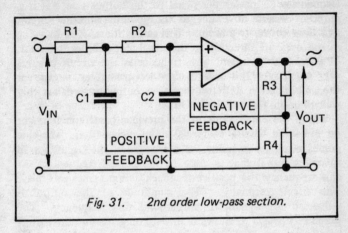

Fig. 31.   2nd order low-pass section.

The first stages of the circuit of Figure 31 are similar to the second-order low-pass filter of Figure 16, except that C1 is connected to the output of the amplifier instead of being grounded.   The important point is that although the amplifier has negative feedback to its (−) input, as in Figure 26, the feedback to the first filter stage is *positive.*   As explained on page 40, negative feedback tends to make a circuit stable. By contrast, positive feedback such as we have here, makes a circuit unstable.   It tends to make it oscillate.

We sometimes experience the effect of positive feedback with a public address system, when the volume is turned up too high and the amplified sound from the loudspeakers is readily picked up by the microphone. The sound reaching the microphone is amplified again and the process goes on and on with increasing volume.   The effect is strongest at certain frequencies so that what begins as a small noise ends as a very loud screeching sound.   The system is *resonating* at that frequency.

45

Now to return to the filter of Figure 31. At low frequencies the capacitors have little effect, since they block the transmission of the signal to ground or to the output side of the amplifier. The signal passes to the amplifier and is amplified or not, depending on the ratio between R3 and R4. At high frequencies C1 passes the signal to the output side, but it is reduced because it passes to the potential divider R3/R4, and then to the (−) input. This causes the output to swing in the opposite direction to the signal and nullifies its effect. Thus at both low and high frequencies the circuit behaves very much as a 2nd order passive low-pass filter, except for the amplification and the increased output impedance that we had in the filter of Figure 30.

Given the conclusions of the previous paragraph it might be wondered what is so special about such a filter. The clue comes when we examine the behaviour of the circuit for an incoming signal that is close to the cut-off frequency. At this frequency the positive feedback action comes into play. The circuit resonates. The amplitude of the output is enhanced for signals at and around that frequency. The graph of V_{OUT}/V_{IN} shows an upward bulge around the cut-off frequency. In fact it has a shape very much like the response of an LC filter (Fig. 24). The crucial part of the response curve, the 'knee', has been sharpened without resorting to inductors.

The extent to which the filter resonates near the cut-off frequency can be controlled by varying the ratio between the two capacitors. If C1 is large compared with C2, resonance is strong and the response curve peaks sharply. We say that the filter is under-damped (Fig. 32). At the other extreme, if C1 is small compared with C2, there is little resonance and the filter is highly damped. In fact its frequency response may be little different from that of a passive filter. By a careful choice of capacitor values the resonance can be controlled so that exactly the right amount of damping occurs. The filter is *critically damped*.

One particular version of the VCVS filter is the Sallen and Key filter. In the Sallen and Key filter the gain of the amplifier is 1. In other words the amplifier is wired as a unity gain amplifier (Fig. 27). The circuit is the same as Figure 31

46

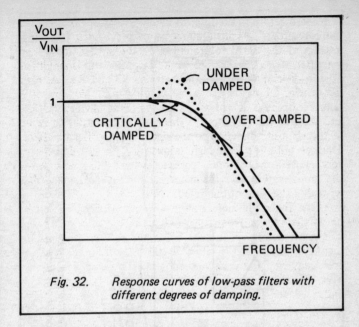

Fig. 32.   *Response curves of low-pass filters with different degrees of damping.*

except that R3 and R4 are omitted and there is negative feed-back directly to the (−) input.

Orders of Active Filters

So far we have described the 1st order and 2nd order sections which have a roll-off in their cut-off regions of −6dB and −12dB per octave. The 2nd order filter introduces the possibility of controlled damping. As with passive filters, we can cascade such sections together to obtain increasing rates of roll-off. A 3rd order filter, for example, is made by connecting the output of a 1st order section to the input of a 2nd order section. The roll-off of this filter is −18dB per octave. In general we make multiple filters of *even* orders (2nd, 4th, 6th, etc.) by cascading one or more 2nd order sections. Multiple filters of *odd* orders (1st, 3rd, 5th, etc.) are made by beginning with a 1st order section and cascading after it as many 2nd order sections as are required. As an example, Figure 33 shows a 5th order low-pass filter made

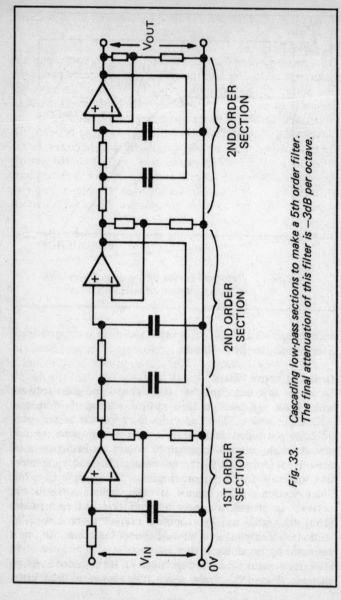

Fig. 33. Cascading low-pass sections to make a 5th order filter. The final attenuation of this filter is −3dB per octave.

48

from a 1st order section followed by two 2nd order sections.

Types of Response
The performance of a multi-section filter depends upon the responses of the sections of which it is composed and, since the output of one section becomes the input of the next, the response of any given section depends partly upon the characteristics of the sections preceding and following it. In designing a multi-section filter the relationships between the sections have to be carefully calculated with reference to the filter as a whole. This means that very often the cut-off frequency will be different for each section, as will the amount of damping. The mathematics involved is complex but, as a result of this, we are able to produce filters with various combinations of desirable characteristics.

The features that define the characteristics of a filter are:

(1)   Cut-off frequency
(2)   Roll-off
(3)   Damping
(4)   Flatness of the pass-band
(5)   Overshoot
(6)   Time delay

We have already dealt with the first three features but must briefly discuss the others. The pass-band of a passive filter is almost perfectly flat; V_{OUT} is equal to V_{IN} until the cut-off frequency is approached (Fig. 13). This is not necessarily the case with multi-section active filters. Interactions and resonances may cause certain frequencies in the pass-band to pass slightly more strongly than others. Thus the ratio of V_{OUT} to V_{IN} within the pass band varies with frequency. This may lead to ripples in the pass band (Fig. 34), the more sections in the filter the more ripples.

Overshoot is the tendency of the output to swing too far when there is a sudden change of input level. It then oscillates for a short while before settling at its final correct level (Fig. 35). Obviously, this is an undesirable characteristic, as it introduces distortion into the output.

When a signal passes through a filter it is subject to a change of phase (page 19), or time delay. The amount of delay varies

49

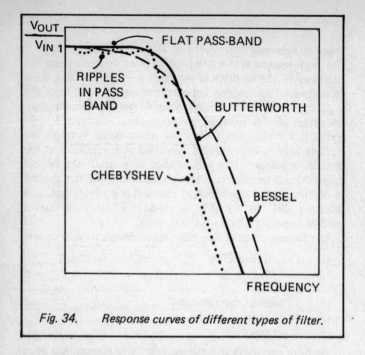

Fig. 34. *Response curves of different types of filter.*

with frequency. As shown, it is clear from Figure 2 that most signals consist of a mixture of a number of waveforms at different frequencies. Filtering imposes a different amount of delay on each component of the signal. The signal emerging from the filter has the same components but their relative timing is different. The effect may be quite small but the result is that the signal is distorted, a factor that may be crucial in certain applications. The effect is more pronounced at lower frequencies.

Well beyond the cut-off region, in the stop band, the slope of the response curve is −6dB, −12dB or more per octave depending only on the order of the filter. It is only necessary to know how steep the curve is intended to be and produce a filter of the required order. It is mainly in the pass-band and the transition region around the cut-off point that design becomes critical. The designing of filters is nearly

50

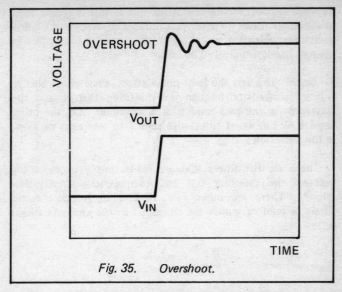

Fig. 35. Overshoot.

always a matter of compromise. For example, the factors that operate in the direction of keeping the pass-band flat also operate to reduce the slope of the curve just beyond the cut-off point. Unfortunately, all that the designer can do is to specify the relative cut-off frequencies and the amount of damping of each section of the filter, and calculate what the resulting response of the filter will be.

There would seem to be an infinite range of possibilities, but most filters fall in one or the other of three main groups:

1 Butterworth filter. The pass band is very flat (Fig. 34), and overshoot is not excessive, but the slope in the transition region is poor. It also has poor phase characteristics. This type of filter is often recommended as the best for general use, owing to its theoretically flat pass-band. However, in practical versions of this filter the effects of tolerance in component values is to introduce ripples in the pass-band and it usually loses its main advantage.

2 Chebyshev filter. This has a steep slope in the transition region at the expense of ripples in the pass-band. Phase

51

response is poor, so that distortion due to this is greater than in the other filters. There are a number of designs of Chebyshev filter, classified according to the depth of the ripples in the pass-band, usually 1, 2 or 3dB.

3 Bessel. This has the least phase effect, since phase change is less dependent on frequency in this filter. Distortion of the waveform in the pass-band is at a minimum. On the other hand it is the worst filter with regard to steepness of slope in the transition region.

These are the filters that are made simply by cascading together the 1st-order and 2nd-order sections already described. There are other ways of building low-pass active filters, several of which are examined in the chapters which follow.

PROJECT 2 – Simple Intercom   *Level 2*
This is a basic intercom circuit but has the special feature of a filter to improve the quality of the sound. Cost is reduced in this project, as in most inexpensive intercoms, by using the loudspeaker to double as the microphone. For the sake of compactness, the loudspeakers used in intercoms are usually of small diameter, and as a result, high frequencies are emphasised and sound tends to be 'tinny'. In this project we use an active low-pass filter to remove the high-frequency components of the signal. The intercom has many uses in the home or office. Since only one station is transmitting at any one time, it is very suitable as a 'baby-listener'.

How It Works
The master station unit contains the main circuit (Fig. 36), the control switch (S1) and the twin 6V batteries which provide the power supply. The slave station consists only of a loudspeaker. Thus it is possible for the master station to call the slave station, but not vice versa. This may be considered a disadvantage by some users but, to others, one-sided control is

a definite advantage. This arrangement has the advantage of minimising the number of components required. A bell or buzzer system can be installed to give two-way calling facilities if this is really essential.

The circuit is based on a single IC which contains four JFET operational amplifiers. We use three of these, the first (IC1a) as a pre-amplifier to condition the signal ready for filtering. The second amplifier (IC1b) is used for the filter, and the third (IC1c) as an output amplifier. In the description, we assume that S1 is switched to position 2, so that the master station is transmitting and the slave station is receiving.

When the user speaks into the loudspeaker LS1, the motion of the loudspeaker coil in the field of the loudspeaker magnet induces an alternating e.m.f. in the coil. This e.m.f. is passed across C1 to the first amplifier which is wired as an inverting amplifier (Fig. 28) with gain variable from 1 to 100. The output from this goes to a 2-pole active low-pass filter, which has a roll-off in the stop band of -12dB per octave. The values of the resistors and capacitors are chosen so as to give a Butterworth response (page 51) with cut-off frequency at about 900Hz. If a slightly crisper tone is preferred, 27nF or 47nF capacitors can be substituted for C2 and C3. Although the filter has a certain amount of gain, we need additional gain to produce a sound audible above a modest background of noise. IC1c, wired as an inverting amplifier with fixed gain of 27 provides this.

The output stage consists of a conventional Class AB push-pull circuit. This consists of two emitter-follower circuits connected back to back. There is no voltage amplification at this stage, but the emitter-followers are capable of providing sufficient power to drive the loudspeaker of the slave station LS2. Only low-wattage (0.2W) speakers are used so the output transistors are rated for 500mA. No heat sink is necessary for the transistors. The function of the diodes is to bias the base of each transistor so that it begins to conduct *immediately* the voltage from IC1c departs from zero. For example, because of the voltage drop across the junction of D1, the base of TR1 is always 0.6V above the output of IC1c. Thus as soon as the output begins to exceed 0V, the base of TR1 is brought above 0.6V and the transistor begins to conduct. If it were not for

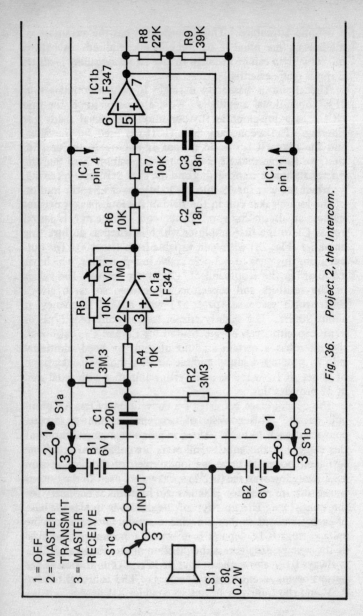

Fig. 36. Project 2, the Intercom.

54

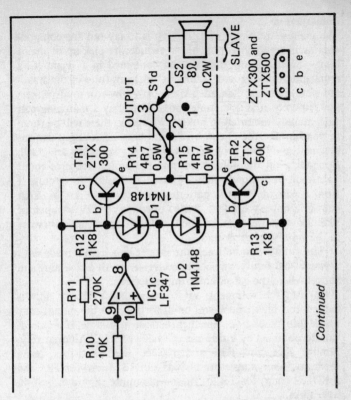

these diodes, neither transistor would conduct until the output of the amplifier was more than +0.6V or less than −0.6V. Small signals (less than ±0.6V) would not be heard at all! Also, there would be a serious distortion of the waveform every time it crossed the zero level.

The rest of the circuit is concerned with controlling the direction of transmission. S1 is a 4-pole 3-way rotary switch. In position 1 both the power lines from the batteries are disconnected and the intercom is off. In position 2, LS1 is connected to the input side of the amplifier system and LS2 is connected to the output. The master talks to the slave. In position 3 the reverse applies, and the slave can talk to the master.

55

Construction

The main point about construction is to lay out the components as compactly as possible to reduce the pick-up of mains hum. Since the op amps are all contained in a single IC, a rectangle of strip-board 100mm × 74.1mm (one of the standard sizes) is more than adequate. Only low-cost loudspeakers are required; it is sometimes possible to buy a matching pair each already mounted in boxes. With luck, there will be room in one box for the circuit-board and batteries. Unless conversations are unduly prolonged, current requirements are small. Depending on the volume setting, the project requires about 15mA on each power line. Thus it is feasible to operate it from a pair of PP1 6V batteries, or from four AA or AAA cells in a battery holder. It also operates on ±9V so a pair of PP3 9V batteries can be used, with an appreciable increase in the volume of the sound.

The connection between the master and slave is made with a pair of light-duty wires. For convenience, fit a jack plug and socket where the cables enter the enclosures.

In use, the volume is set by adjusting VR1. If this is turned too high, there will be distortion and the circuit may break into oscillation. Further increase in volume, if required, can be obtained by increasing the value of R11. Alternatively, remove R14 and R15 and replace the transistors, using medium-power transistors such as a BD131 (npn) for TR1 and a BD132 (pnp) for TR2. These will require clip-on or bolt-on heat sinks.

Special Components

Semiconductors

D1, D2	1N4148 silicon signal diodes (2 off)
TR1	ZTX300 npn transistor
TR2	ZTX500 pnp transistor

Integrated Circuit

IC1	LF347 (or TL-074) quad JFET op amp

Miscellaneous

LS1, LS2	8-ohm 0.2W miniature loudspeaker, approx. 50mm diameter recommended, though any 'spare' 8-ohm speaker could be used, or even 4-ohm or 15-ohm (2 off)
S1	4-pole 3-way rotary switch, with knob.

Chapter 5

HIGH-PASS ACTIVE FILTERS

In Chapter 3 we saw how a low-pass passive filter may be converted into a high-pass filter simply by exchanging the resistors and capacitors. Figures 16 and 17 illustrate this point for second-order passive filters. An active low-pass filter is converted into its equivalent high-pass version by employing the same procedure. For example, the second-order low-pass section of Figure 31 becomes the high-pass section shown in Figure 37. Note that only the resistor-capacitor networks of the section are involved in the exchange. The two resistors in the negative feedback loop naturally remain as resistors since they constitute the potential divider which determines the amount of feedback.

The operation of the high-pass filter is the converse of that of the low-pass filter, described on page 35. At high frequencies the capacitors pass the signal directly to the op amp. It is amplified according to the relative values of R3 and R4 and finally appears at the output. At low frequencies the capacitors block the passage of the signal to the amplifier. Instead, the signal is partly routed through R1 to the output side of the amplifier and partly through R2 to the ground line. The low-frequency signal going to the ground line is lost. The

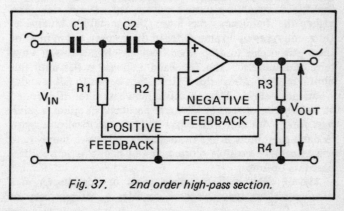

Fig. 37.   2nd order high-pass section.

signal coming through R1 is largely cancelled owing to the effect of negative feedback. At both high and low frequencies the section behaves in much the same way as a second-order passive filter, except that amplification may restore or enhance the signal level. As in the low-pass filter of Figure 31, there is strong positive feedback around the cut-off frequency. Resonance occurs, giving an upward thrust to the response curve. In this way the operational amplifier is made to produce the same sharpening of the knee of the curve as would be obtained by using an inductor.

Apart from filtering out low frequencies instead of high frequencies, high-pass filters have very similar properties to their low-pass counterparts. The frequency of the cut-off point is given by the equation $f = 1/2\pi RC$. The roll-off in the stop-band is +6dB for a first order section and +12dB per octave for a second order section. The positive sign indicates that V_{OUT}/V_{IN} *increases* with increase of frequency. First-order and second-order sections may be combined to produce filters of higher orders. Finally, by suitable choice of capacitor values we may build filters with a range of responses such as Butterworth, Chebyshev, Bessel and others. But there is one difference due to the nature of operational amplifiers. The gain of an op amp falls off when frequency is in excess of a given level. This is because voltage levels and currents in an amplifier can never change instantaneously (page 40). Everything takes time to happen. Consequently there is a limit to the rate at which the output voltage can rise and fall. The higher the frequency, the lower the amplitude attainable. Different types of op amp differ in this respect, but in most of them gain begins to drop when frequency is in excess of a few tens of kilohertz. The pass-band response is flat until this limit is reached. Above this limit, output begins to fall at about −6dB per octave. Thus an active high-pass filter, if operated at frequencies of tens of kilohertz becomes, in effect, a *band-pass filter*. We deal with filters that are specifically designed as band-pass filters in the next chapter. Here we simply note this effect as a possible shortcoming of high-pass active filters based on op amps.

Having dealt with the main topic of this chapter in a relatively short space we now consider a different way of building active filters using op amps.

Frequency-dependent Negative Resistors

An FDNR, as it is more conveniently known, is a sub-circuit which behaves as if it has negative resistance. The value of its negative resistance depends on the frequency of the signal that is being applied to it. Obviously such a sub-circuit could have applications in filtering.

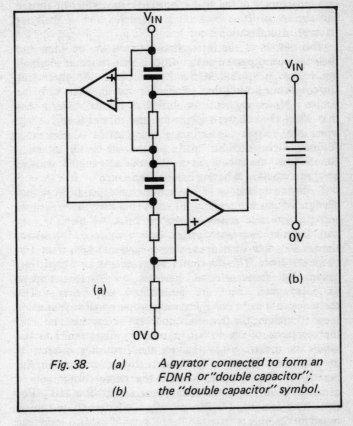

Fig. 38.   *(a)*   *A gyrator connected to form an FDNR or"double capacitor";*
             (b)   *the "double capacitor" symbol.*

The FDNR is one of several variants on a type of sub-circuit known as a *gyrator*. As Figure 38 shows, a gyrator consists

61

of two op amps taking their inputs from and supplying their outputs to a chain of five elements, usually resistors and capacitors. Each op amp feeds its output through this chain to the inputs of the other op amp. Their interactions run round and round in circles, hence the name gyrator. An element in the chain can be any device that has reactance but, if the first and third elements are capacitors and the others are resistors, we have a sub-circuit with the property of negative resistance. As might be expected, the swings of voltage and current in this sub-circuit are complex and we shall not attempt an explanation here.

The output of the interaction between the op amps and their associated passive components is that, when an alternating voltage is applied at the V_{IN} terminal, the alternating current flowing into that terminal is *out of phase* with the voltage. Moreover, the phase difference is 180°. This means that when the voltage is increasing, the current is decreasing; when the voltage is decreasing, the current is increasing. Although the individual parts of the sub-circuit all obey Ohm's Law, the sub-circuit as a *whole* acts in this unusual way, equivalent to it having negative resistance.

Since the behaviour of the sub-circuit depends on several changes of phase internally, brought about by the capacitors and the inverting action of the op amps, we might expect that negative resistance varies with frequency. Negative resistance is low when frequency is high and high when frequency is low. The sub-circuit acts similarly to a capacitor, passing high frequencies and blocking low frequencies (page 8). However, there are quantitative differences. The reactance of a capacitor is inversely proportional to frequency (page 9); halving the frequency doubles the reactance. Because the reactance of the FDNR is inversely proportional to the *square* of the frequency, halving the frequency *quadruples* the reactance. So the FDNR has a stronger action than the capacitor. Furthermore, whereas the phase change with a capacitor is 90°, the phase change with an FDNR is 180°. For these two reasons, FDNRs are often referred to as 'super-capacitors'. This is reflected in the symbol used to represent FDNRs in circuit diagrams (Fig.38(b)).

The properties of FDNRs lend themselves to the production

of filters with flat pass-bands and precisely determined phase response. In addition, component tolerances have relatively little effect on the behaviour of the sub-circuit. For these and other reasons FDNR filters are becoming popular, especially in instrumentation where high-quality reproducible filtering is essential.

PROJECT 3 – Infra-red Intruder Detector   *Level 2*
Although this project was designed for detecting intruders, it has many other uses as a domestic 'watchdog'. It can check that toddlers have not wandered out through the open back door; it can check that a likely sleep-walker has not strayed from their bedroom; it can make sure that the cat has come in; it can watch for the postman.

How It Works
The device depends upon the familiar 'broken beam' principle but with the refinement that the beam is pulsed. The transmitter produces 1000 pulses a second, but each pulse lasts only for 0.1ms. In other words the 'duty cycle' is 0.1. The infra-red LEDs are switched on for only 10% of the time. This means that they can be made to carry a very heavy current during that short period, emitting short but intense pulses of infra-red. This gives the transmitter a very much longer range than would be obtainable with a continuously emitted beam. It also means that power consumption is only one-tenth of what it would otherwise be. In the transmitter there are three LEDs wired in parallel and each carries a current of about 660mA when switched on. This gives a total current requirement of 2A when the LEDs are on, but an *average* current of only 200mA.

The other benefit of using a pulsed beam is that the receiver can be designed to respond only to a pulsed signal. This means not only that the alarm sounds when the beam is broken, but also that the alarm sounds if any attempt is made to saturate the sensor by shining a bright light on it. Since the system operates with infra-red, it makes it impossible for the intruder to see the beam and avoid it, even in total darkness.

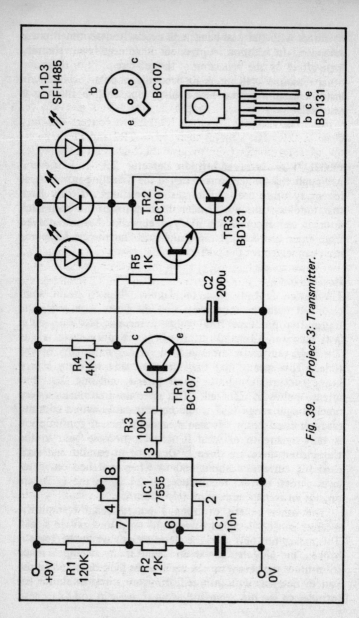

Fig. 39. Project 3: Transmitter.

64

Indeed, an intruder shining a flashlight around the room is very likely to trigger off the alarm without even stepping through the beam.

The transmitter (Fig. 39) is based on a timer IC which produces a signal at 1kHz, with a duty cycle of 0.9. The output of the timer is high for approximately 0.9ms and low for 0.1ms. This signal is inverted by TR1 to convert the duty cycle to 0.1. The signal is then fed to TR2 and TR3 connected as a Darlington pair to give the high gain required to switch the infra-red diodes on and off. TR3 is a medium-power transistor, able to carry the heavy peak current required. In order to meet the sudden demand for a large current every time the LEDs are switched on, a high-value electrolytic capacitor C2 is wired between the power lines. This accumulates charge while the LEDs are off, ready for the relatively short period during which the current is required.

The receiver (Fig. 40) uses an infra-red photodiode D4 as its sensor. The diode is reverse-biased and only a small leakage current flows. The amount of leakage current is proportional to the amount of illumination reaching the diode. As the leakage current flows through R6, a potential difference is generated across it. Thus the received signal appears as a pulsed voltage, which passes through R9 to the operational amplifier IC2a. This has a gain of 330, giving an amplified signal which is then filtered by the high-pass filter based on IC2b. The values of C3, C4, R11 and R12 are chosen to give a cut-off point at about 800Hz. The reason for using a high-pass filter is that the signal may be subject to changes at low frequency. There may be variations in the amount of light (both visible and infra-red) reaching the photodiode from sources other than the transmitter. For example, closing the curtains at dusk causes a sudden reduction of light level which affects the sensor. This is a slow (low frequency) change which, though it affects voltage level at the output of the amplifier, has no effect at all on the output of the filter. There is also the problem of the 50Hz signal emitted by mains-powered lamps. In addition it is possible for 50Hz mains interference from other equipment in the room to be picked up and amplified by the circuit. Signals at 50Hz from whatever source are removed by the high-pass filter.

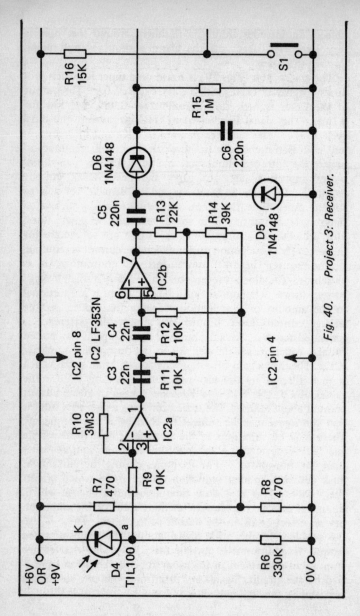

Fig. 40. Project 3: Receiver.

66

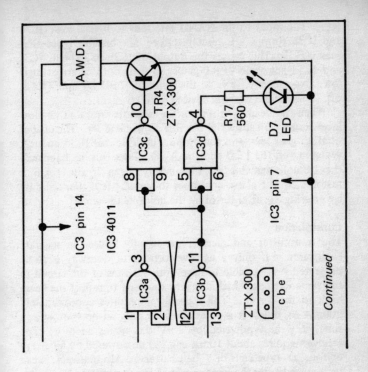

The filtered signal now passes across C5 to a *diode pump*. This is a sub-circuit which responds only to a pulsed signal. Like most water-pumps and air-pumps it has two 'valves', the two diodes D5 and D6. As the potential at C5 increases, current flows through D6 and charges capacitor C6. As the potential at C5 falls, current passes from the 0V line through D5 to prevent the potential at C5 from falling. Thus, every time a pulse appears at C5 an additional charge is built up on (or pumped into) C6. The charge can leak slowly through R15 but, as long as a continuous stream of pulses is arriving, the charge is maintained. This gives the equivalent of a high logic level at the input of the NAND gate, IC3a. If the infra-red beam is interrupted, or if the sensor is saturated by shining a bright light on it, the output from the filter is no longer pulsing. There is no pumping action and C6 discharges through

67

R15. The input to the NAND gate falls to logical low. IC3a and IC3b form a set-reset bistable. The bistable is reset by pressing S1. This causes the output of IC3b to go high. IC3c and IC3d act as INVERT gates, so their outputs are at logic low. No current flows to the indicator LED D7 and TR4 is off. The audible warning device (AWD) is silent.

When the beam is broken or the sensor is saturated, the low level across C6 causes the bistable to become set. The output of IC3b goes low, and the outputs of IC3c and IC3d go high, switching on the LED and the AWD. Once this has happened the bistable remains set indefinitely, even if the beam is restored, so the alarm continues to sound. It is silenced only by pressing S1, after restoring the unbroken beam.

Construction

The transmitter and receiver are usually housed in separate enclosures. If only a narrow corridor or doorway is to be protected it is possible to have both sections of the circuit in the same enclosure with a mirror opposite to reflect the beam back to the sensor. The transmitter requires approximately 200mA so, unless it is to be used for only an hour or so at a time, it is best powered by a 9V d.c. mains adaptor. The receiver requires about 10mA and can be powered by a battery of four 'D' type cells or a 'bell battery'. Alternatively, it can be powered from the same source as the transmitter.

Before beginning construction, some thought must be given to where the transmitter and receiver are to be mounted. It is much better if both can be concealed from sight, perhaps by being built into existing furniture or cupboards. It may even be possible to disguise one or both units as 'books' on a conveniently sited bookshelf. Use can also be made of window curtains to partly hide them. If a doorway is being protected, locate the units so that they can not be seen until the intruder has actually entered the room. The receiver must be mounted so that it does not receive bright light, either from direct sunlight or from a bright sky, for this would permanently saturate the sensor. If the field of view of the sensor is restricted by placing it at the rear of a narrow tube with a matt black interior, there is less interference from ambient lighting. The range of the receiver is 2m–3m, which is enough for protecting a doorway, a corridor, a hallway or a small room. Range can be extended by increasing the number of diodes in the transmitter to four. Alternatively, increase the range by placing a lens in front of the sensor to focus a larger proportion of the beam on to it. A cheap magnifier of glass or plastic is suitable; better are the inexpensive red plastic lenses specially intended for focusing infra-red. This is yet another way of reducing interference from other sources of illumination.

Another point to consider is the nature of the audible warning device. A wide range of solid-state devices are available, ranging from small pcb-mounting bleepers to weather-proof sirens suitable for mounting on the outside wall of the house. Many of the sirens require a surprisingly small current (about 20mA) for the volume of sound produced. For a security system it is usually better to instal a loud siren and to mount this at some distance from the protected area, preferably in some inaccessible place. Try to conceal the wiring as far as possible. For some of the more domestic purposes mentioned earlier, a low-volume bleeper is preferable. Some of these produce a continuous note, but those that produce a warbling or intermittent sound are usually more effective in gaining attention. Depending on the application these may be mounted on the same pcb or stripboard as the receiver circuit.

When the transmitter is operating, the metal tab of TR3 becomes hot to the touch. It is preferable to fit a clip-on heat sink to this transistor. Mount the three LEDs so that they are side by side and aligned in the same direction. It is sometimes possible to check the circuit by seeing that each LED glows a dull red in the dark. Otherwise, connect a voltmeter to measure the voltage at the collector terminal of TR3. This gives a reading of about 7V, showing a voltage drop of 2V across the LEDs.

Note that D4 is connected so as to be reverse-biased, with its *cathode* (k) positive. The early stages of the receiver can be checked using an oscilloscope. The signal can be monitored at the anode of D4, and (inverted) at the output of IC2a. Both of these signals show the pulses superimposed upon a d.c. voltage which varies with the total intensity of illumination falling on D4. The signal at the output of IC2b shows only the pulsed waveform, though this is *not* a square wave but a series of negative-going spikes. The remainder of the circuit may be checked without an oscilloscope. The voltage across R15 rises to about 4V when the signal is being received and falls almost to 0V when the beam is broken.

When testing and setting up the circuit, it is best if the AWD is not connected. Instead we rely on D7 to indicate whether or not the bistable has been triggered. With the transmitter switched on and aimed at the sensor, D7 goes out and stays out when S1 is pressed and released. Breaking the beam, or shining a torchlight on to the sensor immediately triggers the circuit and D7 comes on. Once the transmitter and receiver have been aligned for correct action, the AWD may be connected into the circuit for final testing. If the circuit is to be used in circumstances in which the transmitter and receiver may frequently need re-alignment, fit a switch between the positive line and the positive terminal of the AWD, so that it may be temporarily inactivated.

Special Components

Semiconductors

D1–D3	SFH485 GaAlAs infra-red emitter diodes (3 off). These are high-intensity diodes with medium beam angle (40°); similar though slightly less powerful types such as TIL38 may be used.
D4	TIL100 photodiode (or similar)
D5, D6	1N4148 silicon signal diode
TR1–TR2	BC107 npn low-power transistor (2 off)
TR3	BD131 npn medium-power transistor
TR4	ZTX300 npn medium-power transistor

Integrated Circuits

IC1	7555 CMOS timer
IC2	LF353 dual JFET operational amplifier
IC3	4011 CMOS quadruple 2-input NAND gate

70

Chapter 6

BAND-PASS FILTERS

The action of band-pass filters was outlined at the end of the previous chapter. Band-pass filters are perhaps the most commonly used type of filter. In a way they have more positive applications than low-pass or high-pass filters. As Projects 1 to 3 have illustrated, the function of low-pass or high-pass filters is usually to remove or reject some unwanted component from a signal. By contrast, a band-pass filter is usually employed to isolate a signal at a particular frequency so that it may be further processed in the absence of interference. Examples of the use of band-pass filters include the tuning circuits of radio and TV receivers, brain-wave detectors, and some of the filters used in musical synthesisers. The projects at the end of this chapter and later chapters emphasise the usefulness of band-pass filters.

As Figure 41 shows, the response curve of a band-pass filter typically has a narrow pass-band with roll-off on either side. The extent of the pass-band is defined by considering that it begins at the −3dB point on the lower roll-off slope and ends at the −3dB point on the upper slope. The *bandwidth* is the difference in frequency of the two −3dB points.

The *centre frequency* is loosely described as the frequency half-way between the lower and upper −3dB points, but we must be clear what we mean by 'half-way'. It all depends on the scales which we use for representing frequency on the response curve. When we refer to roll-off, we express it as so many decibels *per octave*. An octave is not a matter of increasing frequency by a standard amount, for example increasing it by a standard 100Hz from 400Hz to 500Hz, or from 1000Hz to 1100Hz. An octave is a *doubling* of frequency, from 400Hz to 800Hz or from 1000Hz to 2000Hz. Thus, we need to work in octaves when we define what we mean by centre frequency. The example illustrated in Figure 42 has the lower −3dB point at 100Hz and the upper point at 1600Hz. This is rather larger bandwidth than a band-pass filter would normally have but the discussion is clearer if we

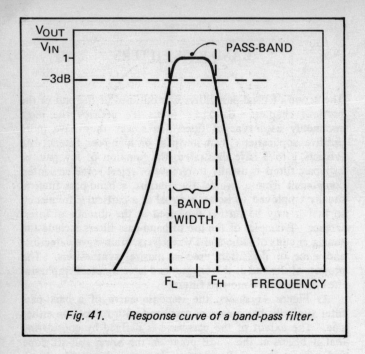

Fig. 41. Response curve of a band-pass filter.

work in whole octaves. In Figure 42 there are 4 octaves between the lower and upper cut-off points (100Hz doubled 4 times brings us to 1600Hz). Putting the centre frequency half-way between the two points *on an octave scale*, it lies 2 octaves above the lower point and 2 octaves below the upper point. Two octaves above 100Hz puts the centre frequency at 400Hz. We can see that this is quite a long way from the average or arithmetic mean of the two points, which is ½(100 + 1600) = 850Hz.

As a general rule for calculation of the centre frequency, we define it as the geometric mean of the upper and lower cut-off points. To calculate the geometric mean of two values we *multiply* them together and then take the square root. Contrast this with the arithmetic mean, in which we *add* them together and divide by 2. In the example of Figure 42, the geometric mean is:

72

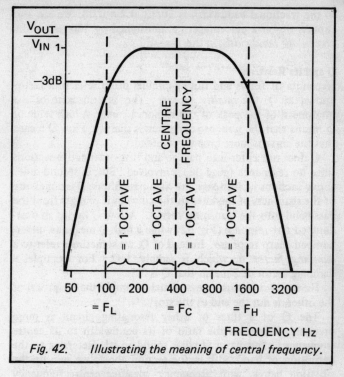

Fig. 42.   Illustrating the meaning of central frequency.

$$\sqrt{(100 \times 1600)} = \sqrt{160000} = 400\text{Hz}.$$

This is the same result as we obtained by counting along the octaves in the figure. More often the upper and lower points are closer together and their distance is some fraction of an octave. Then the geometrical mean equation is the only way of finding the central frequency. For example, if the two points are 1200Hz and 1250Hz, the centre frequency is given by $\sqrt{(1200 \times 1250)} = \sqrt{1500000} = 1224.7\text{Hz}$.

We may sometimes wish to express the bandwidth relative to the central frequency. There are two ways of doing this. One is to express it as the *fractional bandwidth*, the bandwidth divided by the centre frequency. In the example just quoted, the bandwidth is 50Hz and the centre frequency is 1224.7Hz,

73

so the fractional bandwidth is 50/1224.7 = 0.04. We can also express this as a percentage, i.e. multiplied by 100 to give the *percentage bandwidth*, in this case 4%.

Q and its Relatives

Accounts of filters and tuning circuits often refer to a factor known as Q, the *quality factor*. This is a measure of the 'sharpness' of the peak of the response curve. A high value of Q means that the response curve bends sharply; a low Q means that the curve is more broadly rounded.

Q does not enter into passive and first-order active sections since no resonance (page 36) is involved. But, in second-order active sections of low-pass and high-pass filters, Q is a measure of the sharpness of the knee of the curve as it plunges from the pass-band into the transition region. A low Q means an over-damped flat response (Fig. 32) while a high Q means an under-damped sharp response. Instead of Q, we sometimes refer to a *damping factor* d, which is simply 1/Q. For example, a damping factor of 2 means that Q is 0.5.

Having two factors, one of which is simply the reciprocal of the other, is not the end of the story.

The Q of a filter or other resonating circuit is more precisely defined as the ratio of its bandwidth to its centre frequency. This has a familiar sound to it! Referring to the definition of bandwidth in the section above, we sum up the situation below, with 'frequency' meaning centre frequency or resonant frequency, as appropriate:

$$Q = \frac{\text{frequency}}{\text{bandwidth}} = \frac{1}{\text{fractional bandwidth}} = \frac{1}{d} .$$

The factor d is usually applied only to low-pass and high-pass filters, while Q is applied to any kind of resonating circuit, including oscillators and those filters which are based on resonating elements.

Overlapping Filters

The simplest way to make a band-pass filter is to cascade a low-pass filter and high-pass filter with suitable cut-off

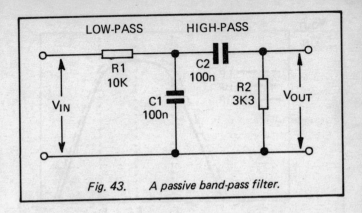

Fig. 43. A passive band-pass filter.

frequencies. Figure 43 shows a passive band-pass filter. With the component values shown, the low-pass filter has its −3dB point at f_H, where:

$$f_H = 1/(2\pi \times 10 \times 10^3 \times 100 \times 10^{-9}) = 159Hz$$

We refer to this cut-off frequency as f_H because it is the higher of the cut-off frequencies, even though it is produced by the low-pass part of the filter. The response curve of the low-pass filter is shown in Figure 44. The −3dB point of the high-pass filter is:

$$f_L = 1/(2\pi \times 3.3 \times 10^3 \times 100 \times 10^{-9}) = 482Hz$$

Figure 44 shows how the response of the high-pass filter overlaps that of the low-pass filter, leaving a pass-band with the centre frequency, f_0, where:

$$f_0 = \sqrt{(159 \times 482)} = 277Hz$$

The bandwidth of this filter is 323Hz and the fractional bandwidth of this filter is 323/276 = 1.1. This gives a reasonably broad pass-band, suitable for most applications. This broadness is indicated by the value of the fractional bandwidth being greater than 1.

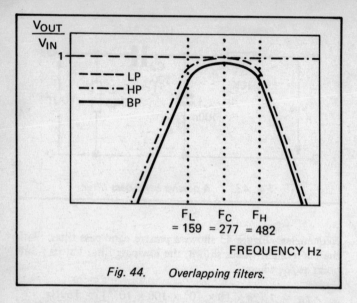

If the components' values are changed so that f_L is raised or f_H is lowered, or both such changes are made, there is less overlap between the curves (Fig. 45). Then the response peaks very sharply, and the signal strength is appreciably reduced in amplitude, a situation which is usually undesirable. The fractional bandwidth is small. As a general rule, filters constructed as in Figure 43 are suitable when the fractional bandwidth is around 1 or greater than 1, but are unsuitable for values significantly less than 1. For such filters we employ active devices in various ways.

Tuned Active Filters

One principle on which a band-pass filter may be based is to use an inverting amplifier with a tuned frequency-rejection sub-circuit in the feedback loop. Figure 46 shows an example of this type of filter. The frequency-rejection sub-circuit is known as a *twin-T*. This refers to the T-shaped configurations of R1, R2 and C1 and of C2, C3 and R3. At the cut-off frequency, the networks shift the phase so that the signals emerging from the twin T's are 180° out of phase and cancel out.

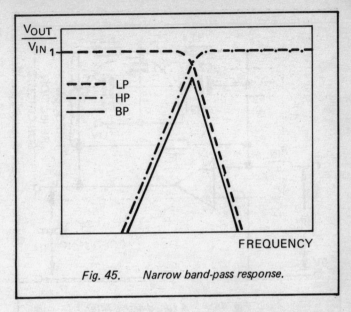

Fig. 45.   Narrow band-pass response.

The result of incorporating the frequency rejection sub-circuit into the feedback loop of the amplifier is that signals of the tuned frequency are not fed back. The lack of *negative* feedback at that frequency results in an increase of gain. Signals are enhanced giving increased amplitude in output at that frequency. This type of band-pass filter is often referred to as a *tuned amplifier.*

This is a useful type of filter but only for a fixed frequency. If it is required to vary the frequency, it is necessary to have a triple-ganged variable resistor, a type of component that is difficult to obtain, particularly as one of the resistors (R3) has to be exactly half the value of the two others.

Multiple Feedback Filters
This is an extension of the overlapping passive filter of Figure 43. The high-pass filter (C1 and R1, Fig. 47) and the low-pass filter (C2 and R2) both receive negative feedback from the output of the amplifier, thus reducing the responses at high and low frequencies. Intermediate frequencies are boosted.

77

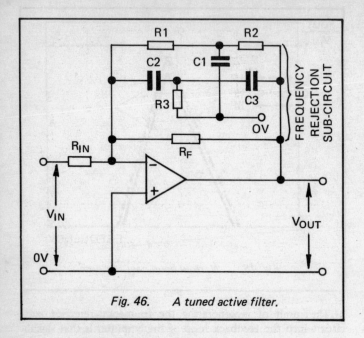

Fig. 46.   A tuned active filter.

VR1 adjusts the centre frequency, without affecting band-width or gain.

The response of a typical filter of this type has high Q, sharply peaked as in Figure 45. For a flatter response band, two such filters are cascaded. They have slightly different (staggered) centre frequencies and together produce a response curve like that in Figure 41. The roll-off is steepened and the peak of the curve is broader (lower Q). If the staggering is increased, that is to say the difference between frequencies is increased, the top of the curve becomes broader still, but a slight dip appears. Provided that this is not too deep, it is usually acceptable.

It is also possible to cascade three or more multiple feed-back filters with staggered frequencies to give an even broader pass-band.

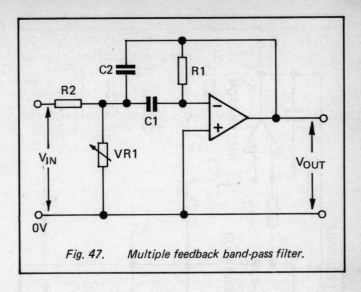

Fig. 47.   Multiple feedback band-pass filter.

State-variable Filters

This is a popular type of filter consisting essentially of an oscillator which is made to oscillate strongly when it is fed with a signal containing its tuned frequency. The circuit consists of a minimum of three op amps, one wired as a *summer* and the other two as *integrators* (Fig. 48). These are two ways of using op amps that we have not described so far. First we consider the summer (Fig. 49). Its action depends upon the *virtual earth* property of the inverting input (page 44). When a number of currents flow toward the inverting input (−), they apparently disappear into it. What actually happens is that these currents combine and flow through the feedback resistor and into the output terminal (which is at negative potential). The op amp adjusts this output potential so that the total current flowing through the feedback resistor is equal to the sum of currents flowing toward the (−) input. This is the only way in which the potential of that input can remain at 0V, equal to that at the (+) input.

If all resistors are equal:

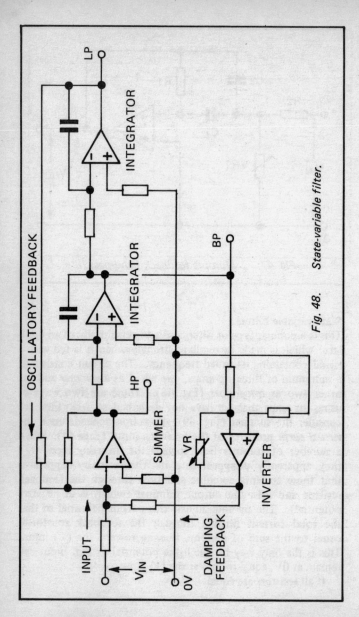

Fig. 48. State-variable filter.

80

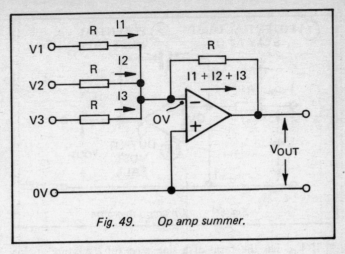

Fig. 49.   Op amp summer.

$$V_{OUT} = -R(I_1 + I_2 + I_3)$$

But $\quad I_1 = V_1/R, \ I_2 = V_2/R \ \text{and} \ I_3 = V_3R$

So $\quad\quad V_{OUT} = -R(V_1/R + V_2/R + V_3/R)$

$$= -(V_1 + V_2 + V_3)$$

The output voltage equals *minus* the sum of the input voltages.

The integrating action of the circuit shown in Figure 50 depends on the fact that the capacitor stores the current flowing to it through R1. If the (−) input is to be kept as a virtual earth, the output potential must fall to accommodate the increasing p.d. between the plates of the capacitor. Thus the output falls at a rate which depends on how much charge is accumulating on the capacitor. It sums or *integrates* the current that has entered the capacitor during the period of time since the current first started to flow. In mathematical terms:

$$V_{OUT} = -\frac{1}{RC} \int V_{IN} \cdot dt$$

81

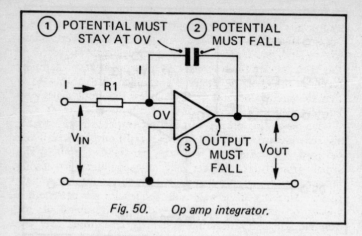

Fig. 50.   Op amp integrator.

If V_{IN} has the form of a sine wave (or a mixture of sine waves of different frequencies), V_{OUT} has the form of the integral of the sine, which is *minus* the cosine. This is equivalent to a sine wave with a phase lag of 90°. If this cosine wave goes to a second integrator, it is integrated again, the integral of minus cosine being minus sine. Now we have the original sine wave, but with a phase lag of 180°. All that remains to be done is to invert this and to recover the original sine wave. All of this happens in the circuit shown in Figure 48. Starting at the middle amplifier in the top row, which is connected as an integrator, any sine wave arriving at this is converted to a minus cosine wave and is then converted to a minus sine wave by the next integrator. This signal is fed back (oscillatory feedback) to the summing amplifier. This inverts the signal and sends it back to the first integrator as a sine wave. If the amount of feedback is sufficient the signal passes round and round the circuit – the circuit oscillates at a frequency dependent on the value of the resistors and capacitors.

The summer amplifier also has a resistor which receives V_{IN}. This is added to the signal (if any) already circulating. If V_{IN} has the same frequency as the resonant frequency of the circuit, it stimulates the circuit to greater oscillation. The signal which appears at the output of the first integrator consists of this resonant frequency – the band-pass frequency.

In this type of state-variable filter the summer amplifier also receives a signal from a fourth op amp, wired as an inverting amplifier. This inverts the band-pass signal (converts minus sine to sine) and feeds it back into the system. The effect of this is to dampen the response. By adjustment of the damping feedback the Q of the circuit is controlled. VR is adjusted so that the circuit does not oscillate unless the input signal contains frequencies in its pass-band.

One interesting property of the state-variable filter is that it also has low-pass (LP) and high-pass (HP) outputs which can be used simultaneously with the band-pass output. The signals from these outputs may be recombined in varying proportions, using an op amp summer, to produce an *all-pass* filter. This is one in which all frequencies are passed to a greater or lesser degree. This allows the response of, for example, an audio amplifier system to be tailored over the whole of the audio spectrum.

Another interesting property of the state-variable filter is that, once it has been made to oscillate, it continues to oscillate for a short time after the stimulating input has ceased. The oscillations die away gradually, like the oscillations of a bell after it has been struck. The length of time depends on the Q of the circuit and may be a second or more. This property is useful when simulating the sound of bells, chimes or vibrating strings (see Project 11).

PROJECT 4 – Tunable Audio Filter   *Level 2*

This is a state-variable band-pass filter (Fig. 51) which can be tuned over a range of frequencies from about 100Hz to 100kHz. It has variable damping and gain. The filter also has low-pass and high-pass outputs. A filter such as this has many applications in the electronics workshop, particularly when designing and building synthesiser and sound effects circuits. It provides an 'instant' filter circuit that can be used to try out sounds and effects, so as to hear what they sound like. When suitable settings have been found by trial and error, a permanent filter with fixed resistors and capacitors can be built to replace the tunable filter.

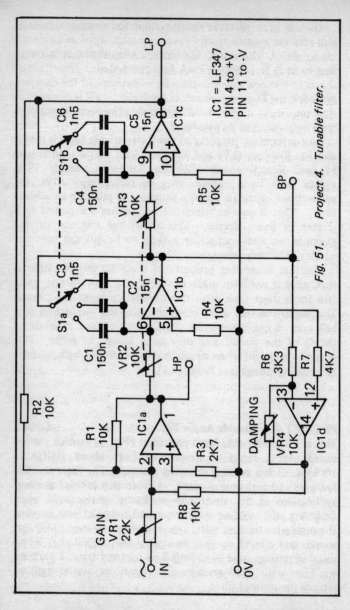

Fig. 51. Project 4. Tunable filter.

Two or more filters of this type may be cascaded to increase roll-off.

As well as the audio applications of this project there are the visual ones, as described in Project 6 below.

How It Works

The operation of this filter has been described on page 83. VR1 is a gain control, the gain ranging from 0.45 when VR1 is set to 22kΩ to 10 when it is set to 1kΩ. VR2 and VR3 are ganged variable resistors sweeping the frequency over a 1:10 range as they are varied from 10kΩ to 1kΩ. There are three ranges obtained by switching different capacitors into the feedback of the integrating op amps. The ranges are:

(1) 106Hz to 1.06kHz
(2) 1.06kHz to 10.6kHz
(3) 10.6kHz to 106kHz

VR4 controls the damping. With VR4 set to 10kΩ the damping factor is 3, or Q = 0.33. At 1kΩ the damping factor is decreased to 0.3 and Q is 3.3. Normally the circuit is in continuous oscillation at this setting.

Construction

The circuit requires a dual power supply of ±5V to ±18V, which is normally supplied from the test circuit. The project is built on a small area of strip-board and housed in a plastic case. One measuring 120mm × 65mm × 40mm was found to be large enough to provide room for the circuit board and for mounting VR1, VR2/VR3, VR4 and S1 on the lid. Compactness of the layout is an asset as this lessens the possibility of interference being picked up from outside sources. The leads for power, input, output (LP, HP and BP) are conveniently terminated with crocodile clips or sprung probe clips.

The switch and variable resistors are fitted with pointer knobs, each of which has a scale. Mark the scales as precisely as possible with the resistance values and capacitor values for each setting. For example, the scale of VR2/VR3 and VR4 is marked to indicate settings of 1, 2, 3, . . . , and 10 kilohm. This is done by measuring the resistance with a test-meter and turning the knob and marking its position for each resistance setting required. These markings enable the user to read off correct resistances and capacitances needed to produce an identical response in a fixed-value equivalent filter. The scales may also be marked with approximate values to indicate frequency, gain and Q. The equations required for calculating these values are:

Frequency:	$f = 1/2\pi RC$	(R in ohms)
Gain:	$A = 10/R$	(R in kilohms)
Q:	$Q = 3.3/R$	(R in kilohms)

One essential point about this circuit is that the input signal must come from a source that has its own internal connection to ground. For this reason the filter can not be coupled to the signal source by a capacitor. If the signal source has no such ground connection, the signal should be fed to the filter by way of an amplifier. This can be any one of the circuits illustrated in Figures 26 to 28. The unity-gain amplifier of Figure 27 is often suitable and is the easiest to build. If it is likely that you will need such an input amplifier frequently it could be built in to the input side of the filter.

Special Components

For greatest reproducibility, fixed resistors should have 1% or 2% tolerance, though 5% tolerance is adequate for less critical purposes. Carbon-track variable resistors are generally suitable if they are calibrated as suggested above. Cermet-track variable resistors can be used for VR1 and VR4, and provide better reliability, but these are not readily available as ganged resistors.

Capacitors present more problems if precision is required. For many purposes the inexpensive polyester capacitors may be used, though their tolerance of ±20% means that precision is very low, unless the capacitors are selected by first measuring their capacitance. Miniature layer polyester capacitors have a better tolerance, usually ±10%. For greater precision, use polystyrene (±2½% or ±1%), though it may not be easy to obtain these in the required values.

The integrated circuit is the LF347 quadruple JFET op amp, for which the TL-074 may be substituted. If you require an extra amplifier as input amplifier (see above), use the single-amplifier version of the LF347, the LF351. If you are using the TL-047 for the filter, use a TL-071.

PROJECT 5 – Audio Signal Generator   *Level 1*

If you do not already have such an instrument, this easily constructed circuit (Fig. 52) provides all that you need for Project 6 below and for some of the musical projects of later chapters. It is also generally useful when building, designing or testing all kinds of audio circuits. The output of the generator is a signal at audio frequencies adjustable from about 50Hz to 2kHz. This does not include the whole range to which the human ear is sensitive but it covers over 5 octaves of the musical scale, from A in the 3rd octave below Middle C (55Hz) to A in the 2nd octave above Middle C (1760Hz). A special feature of this generator is that the waveform can be switched to square wave, pulsed wave, triangular wave, sawtooth wave and sine wave. With these features, the generator is ideal as the basis of an elementary musical synthesiser.

How It Works

The complex parts of this circuits are contained in IC1 (Fig. 52), the 8038 function generator. This not only produces square waves and triangular waves but builds up sine waves, section by section, to a high degree of accuracy. The waveform is selected by switch S1. The frequency range is determined by the values of the timing capacitor C2, and the timing resistors switched between the positive rail and pins 4 and 5. With S2 in position 1, the two 2.2kΩ resistors are switched in. This gives the waveforms a symmetrical shape, so they are true square, sawtooth and sine waves. When S2 is in position 2, the resistance connected to pin 4 is about 5kΩ, while that connected to pin 5 is only 820Ω. This gives an asymmetrical shape to the waveforms. The square wave now consists of long pulses, separated by short intervals about one-sixteenth of the pulse length. This is referred to as a

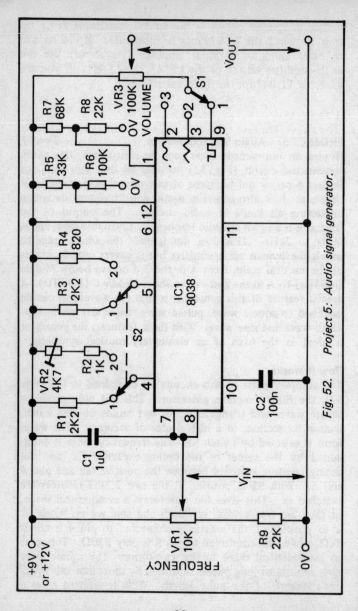

Fig. 52.   Project 5:   Audio signal generator.

pulsed waveform. Asymmetry of the triangular wave converts it to a sawtooth wave, one that can be subsequently filtered to simulate the sound of several different musical instruments (Chapter 8). The sine wave is modified too and may produce effects that are interesting, even if unpredictable.

Construction

The circuit requires only 6mA at 9V or 7mA at 12V so can be powered by a 9V PP3 battery and housed in a very small enclosure. Alternatively you may have plans to build it into a synthesiser project. As part of a synthesiser, the frequency control voltage is provided by keyboard circuits so VR1 and R9 will not be needed. Instead, pins 7 and 8 are simply joined together and the control voltage applied to pin 7.

To test the completed circuit, connect its output to an oscilloscope, to an audio amplifier (page 104) or to a crystal earphone (Fig. 53). It may be possible to hear only the

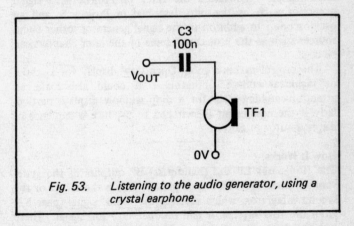

Fig. 53.   *Listening to the audio generator, using a*
crystal earphone.

square-wave signal when using the earphone. The function of VR2 is to adjust the total resistance of VR2 and R2 so that the frequency remains unchanged when switching from position 1 to position 2. Listen to the signal (or watch it on the oscilloscope) while switching between the two positions. Adjust VR2 until there is no difference in frequency.

The precise shape of the sine-wave is controlled by the voltages applied to pins 1 and 12. The potential-dividers R5/R6 and R7/R8 usually provide the correct voltages. If you have an oscilloscope and find that the sine wave is not perfectly shaped, substitute resistors of slightly different values.

If you decide to calibrate VR1 for frequency, the simplest course is to use an oscilloscope and find the settings of VR1 for a range of frequencies. The scale may be marked in hertz or by the notes of the musical scale. Another method is to calibrate the generator against tones produced by a musical instrument such as a piano, or by a set of tuning forks.

PROJECT 6 – Fascinating Phases   *Level 2*

This project investigates the enchanting world of phase relationships. You need the filter of Project 4, a signal generator such as the one described in Project 5, and an oscilloscope. In addition to the signal generator, other audio sources such as the projects of some of the later chapters can be used.

The project makes a good 'Open Day' display for a school or technical college laboratory. It could also make an attention-catching item for a shop window display, particularly if the equipment is switched to produce a sequence of displays automatically.

How It Works

The (low-pass) LP and (band-pass) BP outputs of the state-variable filter are 90° out of phase. This is the effect of the second integrator, which receives the '−cos' signal (page 82) from the first integrator and produces a '−sin' signal. These two signals are applied to the x-input and y-input of an oscilloscope (Fig. 54). The y-input controls the vertical movement of the electron beam that produces the trace on the screen. This is the input to which we normally connect an input signal. Horizontal movement of the beam is usually controlled automatically by a sweep generator circuit inside the instrument. This is set to sweep at different rates to produce the

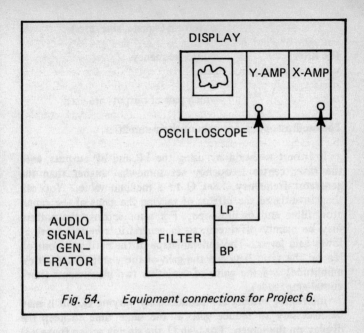

Fig. 54. Equipment connections for Project 6.

various time-bases. Almost all oscilloscopes have provision for switching out the sweep generator and instead controlling horizontal movement directly by an external signal. This is the second input used in this project (Fig. 54).

The interaction between the waveforms from the BP and LP outputs of the filter cause the beam to be swept both vertically and horizontally. In the simplest instance, if the input signal is a pure sine wave, and the amplitude is equal along both axes, the figure produced is a circle. However, there are many parameters that can be independently varied, producing an almost inexhaustible range of patterns on the screen.

Investigating Phase Effects

The variables that determine the patterns are:

The signal generator: frequency
                                   amplitude (gain)

waveform (square, sine, etc.)

The filter: centre frequency
                           gain
                           Q
                           which pair of outputs are used

The oscilloscope: gain of the y-amplifier.

It is best to begin by using the LP and BP outputs, with
the filter centre frequency set somewhat higher than the
generator frequency. Set Q to a medium value. You can
then investigate the effects of varying the gains of the generator, filter and oscilloscope. For some settings the pattern
may be mainly off-screen, so in general it is best to work at
lower gain levels. The general shape of the pattern is controlled by the ratio between the gain of the y-amplifier (vertical
amplitude) and the gains of the other two instruments (horizontal amplitude).

Interesting effects are produced by varying Q, but it may
be necessary to reduce gain at the same time to keep the
display on the screen. For high Q, the ringing action (page 83)
produces a rapidly changing series of patterns. The ringing
action may often be induced either by switching from one
wave-form to another, or by rapidly altering the gain of the
filter.

Although the combination of LP and BP inputs produces
the most involved traces, interesting effects are obtainable by
using BP with HP and HP with LP. The latter pair, being 180°
out of phase, tend to produce diagonally oriented patterns.

As well as using a signal generator, other audio sources may
be employed including the output from a tape-player. The
effects are best when the music has a strong beat and when
few instruments are playing. Solo guitar produces good
results. It makes the display more effective if it can be
arranged for the music to be heard at the same time as it is
being 'seen'.

Chapter 7

NOTCH AND OTHER FILTERS

The idea of a notch filter, or *frequency rejection circuit* was first mentioned on page 76 in connection with one type of band-pass filter. In essence, the notch filter is the converse of a band-pass filter for it passes all frequencies *except* for those in a relatively limited band. One common application of the notch filter is to remove interference at mains frequency (50Hz) from audio circuits and from circuits used in medicine for monitoring low-frequency signals from the human body.

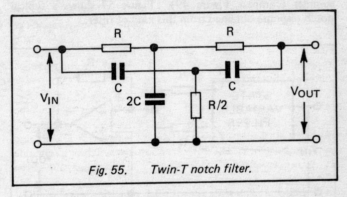

Fig. 55.   Twin-T notch filter.

Figure 55 shows a passive notch filter, the twin-T filter, which has already been seen as part of the circuit of Figure 46. The centre frequency of this circuit is $f_0 = 1/2\pi RC$. This is the frequency at which the signals passing along the two networks become 180° out of phase with each other and therefore cancel out.

Because of the cancelling-out effect, the response curve of a passive notch filter shows a distinct and narrow dip at, and close to, the centre frequency. At frequencies on either side of the centre, the slope the curve flattens out rapidly. In other words, bandwidth is relatively wide. There is also the problem that the performance of the filter depends very much on the precision of the values of the three resistors and three capacitors. Finally, it is not easy to build a tunable notch filter of this type owing to the difficulty of obtaining a triple-ganged variable resistor with the right combination of resistances.

Active notch filters have better responses than passive filters and can be built from state-variable filters of the type shown in Figure 48. If we take the low-pass output from a state-variable filter and add it to the high-pass output, the resulting response has its lowest point at the cut-off point. This is at the frequency at which the signal from the low-pass and high-pass outputs are exactly 180° out of phase (page 82). Figure 56 shows the state-variable filter with its high-pass and low-pass outputs being summed by an op amp, wired as a summer (compare Figure 49). Figure 57 shows a typical notch response obtained from this kind of filter.

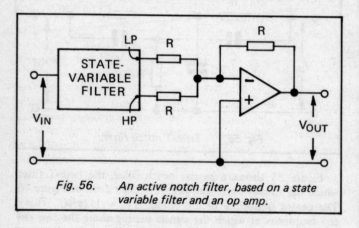

*Fig. 56.   An active notch filter, based on a state
variable filter and an op amp.*

To make a tunable notch filter we base it on a tunable state-variable filter. We begin with a design such as Figure 51, replacing the variable or switchable components with fixed-value components for those parameters which we do not wish to vary. With an appropriate pair of capacitors permanently wired in, the frequency can be swept over a 10:1 range by simply using the dual-ganged variable resistor (VR2/VR3). Dual-ganged variable resistors are relatively easy to obtain.

94

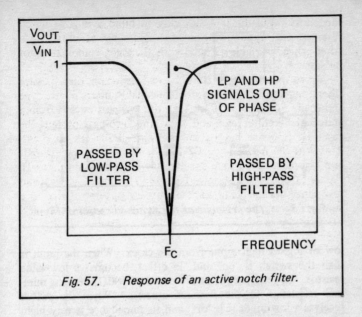

Fig. 57.   Response of an active notch filter.

The filter just described is manually tunable, but there are many applications in which the filter must be electronically tunable. For this purpose we require an electronically tunable state-variable filter. Below we examine a filter of this type, which is used to build the notch filter for Project 7 at the end of this chapter. Another type of electronically tunable filter is described in Chapter 9.

Switched-capacitor Filters
This is a different type of active filter, based on the principle illustrated in Figure 58. Two capacitors and two switches are connected as shown. The switches are under the control of a clock circuit that operates at high frequency, usually several kilohertz. The clock opens and closes the switches alternately. When S1 is open, S2 is closed, and the other way around. Obviously the switches used in this filter can not possibly be ordinary mechanical switches. They are transistor switches, usually field-effect transistors of the type referred to as *analogue switches*. They are controlled by receiving a logical

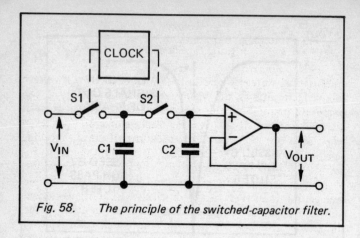

Fig. 58. The principle of the switched-capacitor filter.

low or logical high input from the clock. When the input is
high the switch is 'on' and, in effect, becomes a low-value
resistor. Its resistance is in the order of 100Ω, offering minimal resistance to the flow of current. When the switch
receives a low input it is 'off' and its impedance is very high,
virtually preventing the flow of current.

The way the circuit works is as follows. Suppose that, at a
given instant, the value of the alternating signal V_{IN} is V_1. S1
is 'on' and S2 is 'off'. Current flows through S1 and charges
C1 until the voltage on C1 is V_1. We are assuming that C1 has
capacitance C_1 small enough to allow it to charge fully to V_1
during the short time that S1 is 'on'. Now S1 is turned 'off'
and S2 is turned 'on'. What happens next depends on what
charge is already present on C2. Suppose that the voltage
across C2 is V_2 and that V_2 is less than V_1. Current flows
from C1 to C2 until both capacitors are charged to the same
voltage, intermediate between V_1 and V_2. Similarly, if V_2
is greater than V_1 the capacitors share their charge, and come
to the same voltage, though in this circumstance the current
flows from C2 to C1.

The charge on C1 starts as $C_1 V_1$ (charge = capacitance ×
voltage) and the charge on C2 starts as $C_2 V_2$. When S2 is
closed the total charge is shared between the capacitors,
and they finish up with equal voltages across them:

96

$$\text{Final voltage} = \frac{\text{total charge}}{\text{total capacitance}} = \frac{C_1 V_1 + C_2 V_2}{C_1 + C_2}$$

This final voltage passes to the op amp, wired as a voltage follower, so this is the value now taken by V_{OUT}. The important point about this sequence of events is that there is a levelling effect. If V_{IN} is rising, each sample of V_{IN} (taken when S1 is on) is averaged out against the effects of preceding smaller samples (V_2). This tends to flatten out the rise in V_{IN} and so V_{OUT} shows a slower rise. Conversely if V_{IN} is falling, V_{OUT} falls too, but at a slower rate. Rapid changes of input voltage are converted to slower changes of output voltage. Slower changes of voltage are less affected. In other words, the circuit acts as a *low-pass filter*, in which low-frequency signals are passed more readily than high-frequency signals.

The action of this circuit is affected by the rate at which the switches are turned on and off, i.e. by the clock frequency. If the clock runs fast, there may not be sufficient time for the capacitors to charge fully. This is equivalent to putting extra resistance into the circuit. The frequency response of the low-pass filter thus depends on the clock rate. It is a *frequency-controlled filter*. This is a very useful property for, in its turn, the clock rate can be controlled by an external voltage. Together the clock and filter become a *voltage-controlled filter*, or VCF.

Switched-capacitor filters have the advantage that they are easy to build. Integrated circuits are available that have all the major components for two second-order state-variable filters, including the capacitors, on a single chip. The popular MF10 filter IC has the three essential building blocks, the summer and two integrators, in switched-capacitor form. It contains two sets of these blocks so two separate second-order filters can be built. The two filters can be cascaded to produce a fourth-order filter using a single IC. All that the user needs to provide is the clock circuit or circuits to set the cut-off frequency of each filter. Also required are a few resistors to set the gain and Q of the filter. By suitably joining the various parts of the integrated circuit it is possible to build low-pass, high-pass, band-pass and other types of filter. The filter can be tailored to give all the well-known responses, including Butterworth, Bessel and Chebyshev.

One point to note is that, since the filter works by a switching action, its output is not *exactly* the same as that which is obtained from a more conventional resistor-capacitor passive or active filter. The output varies *step-wise*, not smoothly. In effect the switching action adds a high-frequency component to the signal. Provided that the clock frequency is much higher than the frequencies present in the original signal, this is of no consequence. But switched-capacitor filters are unsuited for use with high-frequency signals.

Transmission-zero Filter

This is a variation on the notch filter. In Figure 56 the signals from the low-pass and high-pass outputs are mixed in equal amounts to produce the notched response. We can also mix them in *unequal* amounts to obtain other responses. In the notch filter the signals flow to the op amp through two identical resistors but, if the resistors have different values, the signals are weighted so that one or the other of the signals predominates in the output from the op amp. All kinds of mixes of the HP and LP signals are possible but one that is of special interest is obtained when we leave the LP signal unchanged and reduce the proportion of the HP signal. This is done by increasing the value of the resistor between the HP output and the op amp.

Taking the extreme case, if there is infinite resistance between the HP output and the op amp, the signal from the op amp is simply the LP signal. Beyond the pass-band the signal level slopes down gently at −12dB per octave (as in a first-order filter). If we mix in a relatively small amount of the HP signal, the effect is to steepen the roll-off curve beyond the LP pass-band (Fig. 59). This type of filter, also known as a *Cauer* or *elliptical* filter, could be called a 'lop-sided' notch filter. It has a notch but, on the high-frequency side of the notch, the signal level is 10 or more decibels lower than on the low-frequency side. On the other hand, if we ignore the high-frequency response, we can look at this as a low-pass curve that falls off much more steeply than −12dB octave. The rate of fall can be adjusted by mixing in a suitable proportion

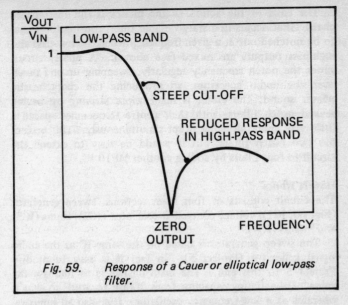

Fig. 59.   Response of a Cauer or elliptical low-pass filter.

of the high-frequency signal. In this way we can produce a low-pass filter with very steep cut-off. The only reservation is that the higher frequencies are present, even though at a relatively low level so, if this raises difficulties, this type of filter can not be used.

A high-pass Cauer filter is made by selecting the resistors so that the high-pass signal dominates the mixture.

PROJECT 7 – Phaser   *Level 2*

A phaser is a device used to modify the sound coming from an electronic musical instrument such as an electric guitar. The result is hard to describe in words but is easily recognisable when heard, and is a popular musical effect. There are a number of ways to produce the effect and in this circuit we make use of a pair of notch filters built around the MF10 switched capacitor filter IC.

The basis of the action of the phaser is the 180° phase change that occurs in a state-variable filter, causing the signal to be notched out at a given frequency when the low-pass and high-pass outputs are mixed (see above). A phaser circuit varies the notch frequency regularly, sweeping up and down over the audio spectrum, so producing the characteristic phaser sound. The effect is made more striking by having several notch filters, with their centre frequencies spaced a little way apart, all being swept simultaneously. This project has two notch filters, but it would be easy to extend the circuit to four filters by adding another MF10 IC.

How It Works
The circuit consists of four main sections: sweep generator (Fig. 60, IC1), voltage-controlled oscillator (IC2), filters (IC3) and mixers (IC4).

The sweep generator is based on the same IC as the audio signal generator (Project 5). In fact it is easy to modify Project 5 to this end. The main change is to increase the value of the timing capacitor from 200nF to 10μF so that it operates as a low-frequency oscillator. It is also an improvement to alter the values of VR1 and its associated fixed resistor so that the frequency of the oscillator may be varied from about 0.2Hz to 10Hz. This controls the rate at which the phasing effect is swept across the audio spectrum, the *sweep frequency*. The square-wave output of IC1 is not required in this application.

IC2 is a phase-locked loop IC, although we use only the VCO part of it in this circuit. The VCO generates the square-wave clock signal that determines the centre frequency of the filters. The frequency of the VCO, the *clock frequency*, f_{CLK}, depends upon the voltage that IC2 is receiving from IC1. With a triangle wave output, the voltage ramps up and down between 3V and 6V at the sweep frequency. When the voltage is 3V, f_{CLK} is about 30kHz. When the voltage is 6V it is about 140kHz. When switched to the sine wave output the sweep frequency ranges between 50kHz and 120kHz. It is possible to lower the sweep range by altering the capacitance of C4 to 2.2nF, should the constructor prefer the effect produced by a lower range.

The resistors connected to IC3 have been chosen so as to give a relatively low gain, to minimise distortion and a low Q to minimise resonance.

Both filters have the same set of resistor values so their outputs are identical. It is the mixing of the LP and HP outputs which produces the two different notch effects. These depend on the relative values of the resistors feeding the two op amps, IC4a and IC4b. For IC4a, the notch frequency is:

$$\frac{f_{CLK}}{100} \times \sqrt{\frac{8.2}{4.7}} = 0.013 \times f_{CLK} .$$

When the clock is swept from 30kHz to 140kHz, the notch frequency is swept from about 400Hz to 1800Hz. This is for triangular waves. The range is less when using the sine-wave output of IC1. For IC4b, the notch frequency is swept from 540Hz to 2500Hz. Between them, the notches sweep across the most-used parts of the musical scale, including the lower harmonics.

The third mixer, IC4c mixes the two notched signals in equal proportions and permits the addition of the original unfiltered signal. By adjusting VR2 the proportion of the original signal can be increased so as to more-or-less swamp the phaser effect, or decreased so that only the phaser signal is heard. The output from IC4c is fed to a high-power audio amplifier. Use a ready-made unit or build one from the many kits available. Figure 61 gives a circuit for a simple audio power amplifier which can be used with this project as well as with other audio projects later in the book.

The controls for this project are summarised as follows:

Sweep-rate (VR1): from 0.2Hz to 10Hz
Depth (VR2): from no phasing effect to maximum effect
Waveform (SW1): triangular (the most distinctive effect)
    or sine wave (softer, with less wide sweeping).

An optional extra control is manual sweep. This consists of a variable resistor, connected as in Figure 62 with a third position on switch S1 to select either automatic or manual action.

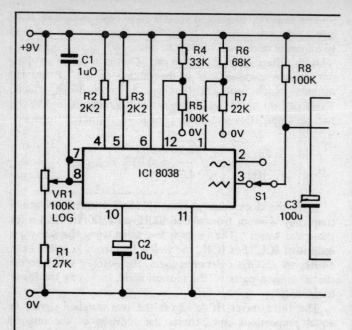

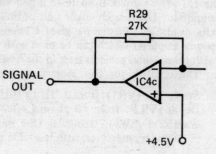

TO +9V: IC3 pins 7, 8
        IC4 pin 4.

TO 0V: IC3 pins 13, 14
       IC4 11.

Fig. 60.   Project 7: Phaser. For optional connections

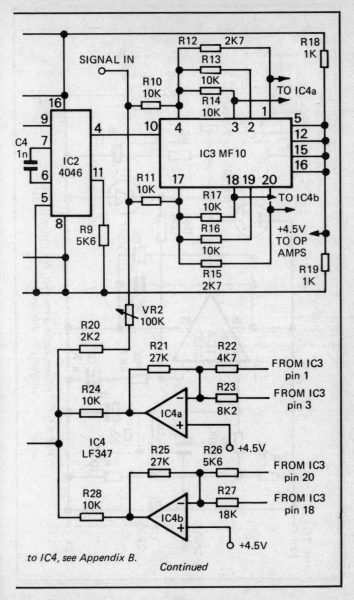

to IC4, see Appendix B.

Continued

103

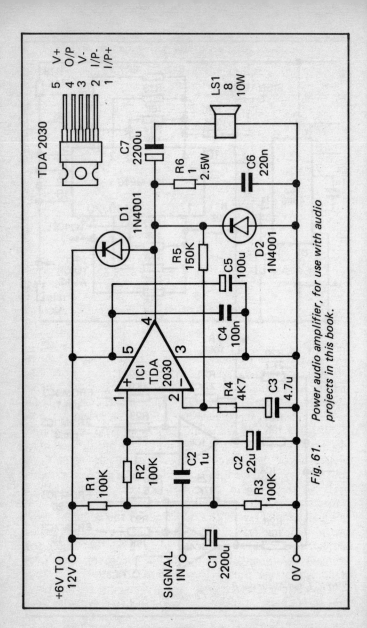

Power audio amplifier, for use with audio projects in this book.

Fig. 61.

104

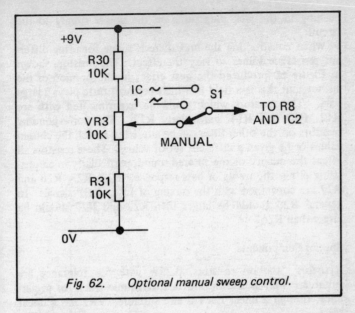

Fig. 62.   Optional manual sweep control.

Construction

The circuit requires about 25mA (excluding power to drive the audio amplifier), which can be provided by a 9V PP3 battery or a mains adapter. Because of the conditions under which the project is likely to be used, the circuit should be housed in a stout metal enclosure. If the case is connected to the 0V line this will reduce the pick-up of hum from nearby electrical equipment. For use with certain instruments it is preferable for the sweep-rate to be controllable by foot. A foot-pedal which incorporates a 100kΩ variable resistor is ideal for this purpose, to replace VR1. An alternative, or possibly additional foot control is a switch inserted into the line between R11 and VR2. This allows the switching in or out of the phaser effect. This could have either a latching or non-latching action, as preferred.   The foot-switch or switches are mounted on top of the enclosure, or a free-standing footswell pedal may be used for VR1.

The enclosure requires two jack sockets, one for input and one for output. Usually the input socket is wired so that pushing in the jack plug turns on the power supply to the circuit.

When constructing the unit there is scope for using different resistance values to vary the effect. The resistors shown in Figure 60 produced the best effect in the opinion of the author, but this is a field in which personal taste plays a large part. The resistors which could be experimented with are R12, R13 and R14, particularly R12. The corresponding resistors on the other filter can be altered to match the chosen values or be given a different set of values. These resistors all affect the quality of the filtered sound, particularly in emphasising either the treble or bass response. R22, R23, R26 and R27 are concerned with the mixing of LP and HP signals. In general R23 should be larger than R22 and R27 should be larger than R26.

Special Components

Resistors   Carbon resistors, 0.25W with 5% tolerance are suitable. VR1 is shown with a logarithmic track for preference, though a linear track is also suitable. VR2 has a linear track.

Capacitors

C4   Polyester or polystyrene capacitor

Integrated Circuits

IC1   8038 function generator
IC2   4046 CMOS phase-locked loop
IC3   MF10 dual switched-capacitor filter
IC4   LF347 quad JFET op amp

The Audio Amplifier

Resistors are 0.25W, except for R6, which is a 2.5W wire-wound resistor. The input lead should be screened, with the screening connected to the 0V line. A compact layout helps avoid interference, except that the input and output sides should not be close together. C4 and C5 are mounted with their terminal wires soldered as close as possible to pins 3 and 5 of the IC. The IC requires a small bolt-on heatsink, rated at about 20°C/W. The loudspeaker must be rated at a minimum of 10W. A multiple speaker unit can be used.

Chapter 8

FORMANT FILTERING

Previous chapters have described different types of filter. This chapter describes a special way in which these types of filter are used. Formant filtering is a way of producing musical effects and is often used in electronic keyboard instruments and electronic percussion sets. Filtering is always a matter of filtering out or *removing* various components of a composite signal. In formant filtering, which is applied only to audio signals, we begin with a signal and remove certain components from it, to give the resultant signal distinctive characteristics. Often the characteristics are those which make the signal sound like a specific musical instrument. However, we also use formant filtering to produce musical sounds that can not be produced in other ways.

Harmonics

Before explaining how formant filtering is done we must describe how musical sounds are produced. One of the simplest ways of producing a musical sound is to pluck a taut string or wire. This is the basis of the guitar. The members of the violin family are played by bowing the string to transfer energy to it and make it vibrate.

A string can vibrate in a number of ways, as shown in Figure 63. The most obvious way is that shown at (a). The frequency of vibration depends inversely upon the length of string vibrating; the longer the string the lower the frequency and the lower the pitch of the note. In (a) the two ends of the string are at rest but the whole string between them is vibrating. This is the maximum length that can vibrate and therefore this is the lowest frequency obtainable, given that other factors, such as the tension in the string, are not to be altered. We call this the *fundamental* frequency, and refer to it as f, measured in hertz.

A string may also vibrate so that not only are its ends stationary but also a point exactly half way between its ends. We call such a stationary point a *node*. This in effect divides

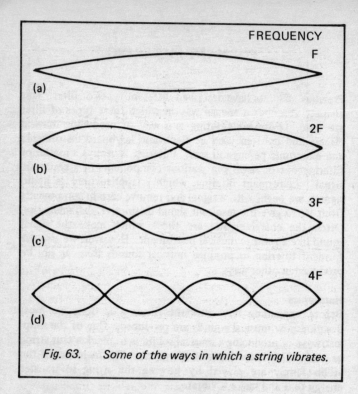

FREQUENCY

F

(a)

2F

(b)

3F

(c)

4F

(d)

Fig. 63.   Some of the ways in which a string vibrates.

the string into two halves (Fig. 63(b)), so the string vibrates with double the fundamental frequency, 2f. A doubling of frequency is referred to as an *octave* (page 22), so the string is producing a note pitched one octave above the fundamental. We refer to this note as the second *overtone*, or second *harmonic*. The string is able to vibrate in both ways simultaneously so it produces both the fundamental and the second harmonic at the same time. The two modes of vibration are not necessarily equal in amplitude; usually the fundamental is the louder of the two.

Figure 63 also shows higher modes of vibration with the string vibrating in thirds (c) and quarters (d). These modes give the third and fourth harmonics with frequencies 3f and 4f respectively. The 4f note is an octave above the 2f note,

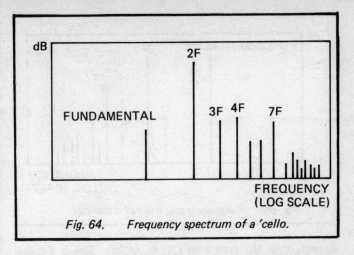

Fig. 64.   *Frequency spectrum of a 'cello.*

and the 3f note comes between them. This is a *fifth* (in the musical sense) in the next octave above the fundamental so that if, for example, the fundamental is C, the 2f note is C′ and the 3f note is G′. The string also vibrates with higher modes (5f, 6f, 7f, etc.), not shown in the diagram.

The relative loudness (or amplitude) of the fundamental and harmonics may be represented in a *frequency spectrum*, as in Figure 64. Here the vertical lines are plotted on a frequency scale, their heights being the relative amplitudes in decibels. In the example shown, the cello, it is noted that the fundamental is *not* the loudest component of the sound. Although the basic sounds originate from the vibrating strings of the instrument, the body of the cello resonates (page 36) at a number of frequencies, thus enhacing certain harmonics but not others. The relative loudness of the harmonics gives the total sound of the cello its own particular timbre, different from that of other stringed instruments. The second harmonic (2f) dominates the sound, while 3f, 4f and 7f are relatively strong. The relative strengths may charge slightly, depending on which note is being played.

Figure 65 shows the spectrum of a clarinet. In this, the fundamental is the strongest component and, for the first few harmonics at least, the odd ones (3f, 5f, 7f) are appreciably

109

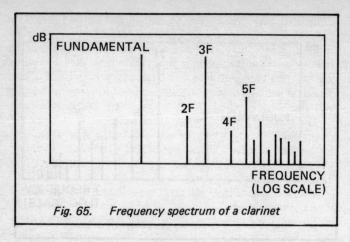

Fig. 65.   Frequency spectrum of a clarinet

stronger than the even ones (2f, 4f, 6f, 8f). This is a consequence of the modes of vibration favoured by the column of air in the clarinet. By contrasting Figures 64 and 65 we begin to see why a cello sounds differently from a clarinet, even if they are playing the same note. On the other hand, the spectrum of a double-bass is very much like that of a cello, making the two instruments difficult to distinguish, except by knowing that the cello plays in a higher register than the bass and has higher-pitched resonances.

Filtering in Action
In order to reproduce the sound of a musical instrument such as a cello, we must begin with a signal that contains the fundamental and all the harmonics. It is preferable that this basic signal is one that is easy to produce electronically. Fortunately, some of the signals that are easiest to produce are rich in harmonics. The square wave is easy to generate but its limitation is that it contains only the fundamental and the odd harmonics (f, 3f, 5f, 7f, etc.). Formant filtering to produce the cello sound involves adjusting the relative proportions of the component frequencies to match the spectrum of Figure 64.

As it happens, few instruments other than woodwinds have a spectrum dominated by odd harmonics, so the square wave is of limited use. As Figure 65 shows, the clarinet produces even harmonics too, so a square wave filtered with a low-pass filter to reduce the higher harmonics does not sound exactly right. One way of improving the realism is to use two square waves, one running at double the frequency (2f) of the other. The double-frequency wave is mixed in at lower amplitude to add the even harmonics (2f, 4f, 6f, etc.) to the spectrum.

The triangle wave is similar to the square wave in harmonic composition, except that there is not such a great reduction in the strength of the higher harmonics. The sound is brassy and can be filtered to give a reasonable simulation of the brass instruments.

The best source that contains both odd and even harmonics is the sawtooth wave. Unfiltered it has a brassy sound and, with band-pass filtering, is used for the trumpet. With a high-pass filter to retain the higher harmonics and slightly reduce the fundamental (Fig. 64), it gives a realistic cello sound. The sawtooth wave is the most useful basic waveform. Another waveform commonly used is the *pulsed wave*, a square wave in which the mark/space ratio is not 1:1. This contains all the harmonics and has a reedy quality.

Further Modifications

Formant filtering is not enough to give a completely realistic effect. Reproducing a typical sound spectrum creates the distinctive timbre but there are other features by which we learn to recognise a specific instrument. Principal among these is the *amplitude envelope*. This is the way in which the amplitude of the sound varies during the playing of a note. Simply to turn the sound signal on and off merely produces a 'beep'. By contrast, the volume of sound from a violin increases gradually as the string is bowed and begins to vibrate. We say the *rate of attack* is slow. What happens next depends upon the intention of the player but usually the amplitude falls slightly from its initial peak; this is the *release* phase. Then it is *sustained* at a fairly constant though lower volume. Finally, when bowing ceases, the volume dies away, or *decays* rather more rapidly. This sequence of attack, release, sustain and decay is met with in all musical sounds, but the rates of change and the duration of each phase may differ. When a note is played on a piano, the string is struck by the hammer and the volume reaches it maximum level almost immediately. Attack is rapid, but decay may be relatively slow, particularly if the dampers are held off the strings. Projects 8 and 9 at the end of this chapter show how the filtered sound is modified in this way to produce a more realistic effect. To simplify the circuits we have concentrated on the attack and decay phases, particularly the former. This is because the human ear (or brain?) is most influenced by the rate of attack, and uses mainly this to identify the apparent source of sound. Although both violin and cello sounds are produced by similar filtering, the attack of the cello is slower than that of a violin, and this is how we distinguish them.

Certain instruments are recognised also by particular features of their sound, often acquired by the method of playing. One well-known feature is *vibrato*, in which the pitch of a sustained note varies slightly up and down regularly while the note is being played. This may be achieved electronically by modulating the input signal to a voltage-controlled oscillator. A low-frequency waveform from an oscillator running at a few hertz is used for this purpose. Another effect is *tremolo*, in which the volume of the sound is varied regularly, as in bells and chimes. In more complex circuits the characteristics of the filter are altered during the period of the sound. For example, the sound of brass instruments is made more realistic if the higher harmonics are present during the attack phase but are filtered out during the decay phase.

Filtering Noise

Many of the percussive instruments, such as the various types of cymbal, the xylophone, the glockenspiel, and the triangle have a very complex sound spectrum. The mode of vibration of these is so complicated that any pattern of regular harmonics may be almost indistinguishable. To a greater or lesser degree their spectra are *aharmonic*. This makes it difficult or impossible to synthesise the sounds of many of them. One approach is to take as the original sound signal one that contains *all* frequencies. This is the purely random hissing noise usually known as *white noise*. This is generated electronically by relying on the random movements of the electrons in a semiconductor, usually in a reverse-biased pn junction, and amplifying the electrical effects of these motions. In the project we use the base-emitter junction of a transistor, but it is also possible to use a reverse-biased Zener diode.

Unfiltered white noise sounds like rushing water or escaping steam. If we filter it and apply an amplitude envelope, we obtain sounds near to those of some of the percussion instruments. Those instruments which have an entirely aharmonic spectrum are the easiest to imitate. Project 9 shows how to simulate cymbals, hi-hat and the sound of a drum being played with wire brushes.

PROJECT 8 – Musical Box   *Level 2*

There are a number of inexpensive ICs that are pre-programmed to play a selection of popular tunes. The simple ones are intended for use in 'musical greetings cards' while the more complicated ones are for use in door-chimes and similar devices. The latter can often be set up so that they play one tune when there is someone at the front door and a different tune for the back door. There are a number of circuits published, either employing these ICs or in some other way producing a short musical output.

Usually the musical signal produced by such devices is a series of square-wave notes or 'beeps'. This project adds another dimension to the sound. The sound is filtered to give it interest, and possibly to make it sound more like a recognnisable musical instrument. For this purpose the circuit incorporates an amplitude envelope generator. The project can be used as the heart of a novel musical box, or it can be used as a door alert or for any purpose where a signal is required on the pressing of a button. It can also be used as a convenient signal source for anyone wanting to try out the effects of various filtering techniques, either as a matter of general interest or with the idea of eventually building them into an electronic keyboard instrument or synthesiser.

How It Works

The description assumes that the musical signal is being

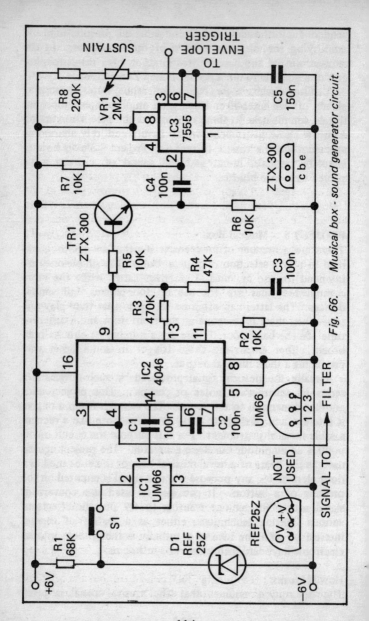

Musical box - sound generator circuit. Fig. 66.

produced by the simplest of the ICs, the UM66. This is available in several versions, each producing a different tune or selection of tunes. The UM66 (IC1, Fig. 66) requires a power supply between 1.5V and 3.5V. We provide it with 2.5V, using the band-gap voltage reference, D1. The tune is played once when power is switched on. To repeat the tune the power must be switched off momentarily. This can be done by turning off the whole circuit, and this method is probably better when the circuit is being used as a door alert. For other applications the optional push-to-break button S1 interrupts the supply to the IC when briefly pressed.

The biggest problem in using signal sources such as the UM66 is that there is no easy way of knowing when each note begins. It is important to know this because otherwise it is not possible to shape the envelope of each note correctly. In this circuit the problem is solved by using a phase-locked loop, IC2. The essential property of a PLL is that it locks on to any signal in its frequency range. The PLL contains a voltage-controlled oscillator which is made to oscillate at the same frequency as the incoming signal. This is done by using a built-in comparator to match the incoming signal against the signal from the VCO. The comparator generates a voltage which is applied to the VCO, through a filter (R3, R4, C3). The input to the VCO (pin 9) is thus varied until the VCO is operating at the same frequency as the incoming signal. If the frequency of the incoming signal changes, or if there is a gap between notes, there is a sudden change in the input at pin 9 until the VCO has been brought into phase with the next note.

This takes only a fraction of a second but, by monitoring the voltage being sent to the input of the VCO at pin 9, we can tell when the input signal changes in frequency. In other words, we can tell when one note has ended and a new note has begun. We use the output of the VCO, at pin 4, as the musical signal. This has the same frequency as the original signal from IC1, and has the advantage that if the original signal is 'noisy' or poorly shaped, it will have been squared up by the VCO.

While a note is sounding, TR1 is held on, but the brief fall in voltage between notes turns it off. This produces a low-going

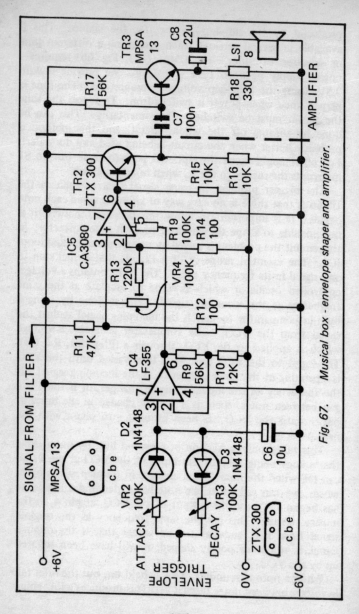

Fig. 67. Musical box - envelope shaper and amplifier.

116

pulse which triggers the next IC into action. This is a timer (IC3) wired to give a single high output pulse of constant length whenever it is triggered. The length of pulse is adjusted by the setting of VR1. When the pulse goes high, current flows through VR2 and D2 (Fig. 67), charging C6. The rate of charge depends on the setting of VR2, which thus determines the attack rate of the note. If the pulse is longer than is required to fully charge C6, the charge on C6 remains steady for the remainder of the pulse; this gives the sustain phase of the note. When the pulse ends, C6 gradually discharges through VR3. The rate of discharge, and hence the rate of decay of the note depends on the setting of VR3.

When a capacitor is charged through a resistor from a supply at fixed voltage, the rate of charge falls off more and more rapidly as the voltage across the capacitor approaches that of the source. This makes it impossible to obtain an attack that rises steeply throughout the phase. This is the reason for using the amplifier IC4. This amplifies the voltage across C6 so that the output from the amplifier corresponds only to the initial stages of charging, during which the voltage is rising rapidly. The discharge phase is relatively unaffected, allowing for a slow decay.

The output of IC4 goes to the control terminal of IC5, which is a transconductance amplifier. The *current* produced by this amplifier is proportional to the difference in *voltage* between its input terminals. The voltage at the (−) input is held steady and the musical signal is presented to the (+) input. The amplitude of the signal current coming from this amplifier depends on the voltage present at the control terminal. Thus the musical signal is modulated by the attack—sustain—decay envelope. Part of the current from IC5 becomes the base current of TR2 which undertakes the first stage of amplification of the modulated musical signal. The second stage of amplification makes use of a Darlington pair, TR3 (shown as a single transistor in Fig. 67). This provides sufficient power to drive a small loudspeaker producing a volume of sound appropriate to a musical box. If a louder sound is required the circuit from C7 onwards can be replaced by the power audio amplifier of Figure 61.

The use of filters in this project has been left to the

117

preferences of the constructor. The output from pin 4 of IC2 can be connected directly to R11, giving an unfiltered tone that is shaped by the envelope generator. This alone is sufficient to produce a different type of sound, illustrating the great importance of the amplitude envelope in synthesising sounds. The sound is given greater interest by connecting a filter between IC2 pin 4 and R11. It is suggested that this stage of development of the project is undertaken on a breadboard, using filters of various types. If a tunable audio filter (Project 5) is available, this can be used to discover the effects of filtering at different frequencies and with differing levels of Q. Chapter 11 describes how to build filters with specified characteristics. Low-pass filtering with cut-off frequency in the region of 1kHz produces the twangy noise of a plucked string, especially if Q is high, with rapid attack, no sustain period (adjust VR2 so that C6 is only *just* charged during the attack phase), and slow decay. If the decay is short the effect is more like that of a blown whistle. The use of a low-pass filter set to a few hundred hertz, with slow attack and decay is another field to explore. Also try a band-pass filter, set to 10kHz, high Q, with slow attack and decay. The sound of a bowed string is obtained by using a high-pass filter set to a few kilohertz, with low Q, slow attack and rapid decay; the main defect in this sound is that there is no vibrato, but this does not matter if the overall length of the note is moderate. More elaborate filtering techniques, such as that used to produce a clarinet effect (page 100) can also be used.

Visual Effects

A musical box may possibly be improved by adding some light-emitting diodes of several colours, flashing in time to the music. There are a number of circuits already published which use band-pass filters to switch on banks of lamps, such as disco-lamps when notes within their pass-band are played. Such circuits can be adapted to flash small filament lamps or LEDs instead. A simple approach is to use the output from IC3 pin 3. Figure 68 shows the circuit to flash one or more LEDs wired in parallel; reduce the resistor value for more LEDs. A relay could be wired instead of the LED and

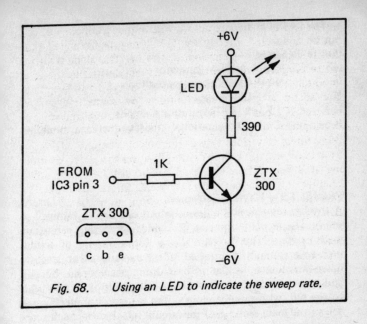

Fig. 68.   Using an LED to indicate the sweep rate.

resistor for switching other devices such as a motor or a solenoid to animate a doll dancing on top of the musical box.

Construction

The circuit requires a dual power supply of ±6V. A pair of 6V battery holders, each with 4 type AA cells is suitable for intermittent use as a musical box or door-alert. It requires about 150mA from each battery when using the power audio amplifier.   For more protracted use a dual mains PSU is preferred. Note that the 0V rail does not appear in Figure 66; all negative-going connections in that diagram are to the −6V rail. If all that is required is to set the envelope once and for all, VR1−VR3 can be preset potentiometers. For experimental applications, use panel-mounting potentiometers, with pointer knobs.

Special Components

Integrated Circuits

IC1   UM66 melody generator
IC2   4046 CMOS phase-locked loop
IC3   7555 CMOS timer
IC4   LF355 JFET operational amplifier
IC5   CA3080 operational transconductance amplifier.

PROJECT 9 – Rhythm Sequencer   *Level 3*

A rhythm sequencer is a device which can be programmed to produce a regular sequence of sounds simulating percussion instruments. This project allows for a variety of sounds including cymbals, a brushed side-drum and other staccato drum-like sounds similar to bass drum, snare drum, bongos, and maracas. The circuit operates on a cycle of up to 8 beats to the bar, with variable tempo. The system diagram (Fig. 69) shows the main sections of the circuit, but there is much scope for adding to this to give even greater programming flexibility or to omit any sections that the reader does not require. This is rated as a 'Level 3' circuit because it has many parts and care is required in planning and laying out the circuit. However, the individual sections of the circuit are simple to build and align, and the beginner could easily start with just a few of the facilities offered and expand the sequencer later.

How It Works

There are two subsections of this circuit:

(1)   Noise-based sounds – e.g. cymbals, hi-hat, brushed drum.
(2)   Filter-based sounds – e.g. drums, blocks.

These sections are both under the control of the clock and counter, and their outputs are combined by a mixer circuit.

The clock generates pulses at a rate that is variable between about 5Hz and 15Hz. The setting of VR1 (Fig. 70) sets the clock rate or *tempo* hence the time of the repeating sequence

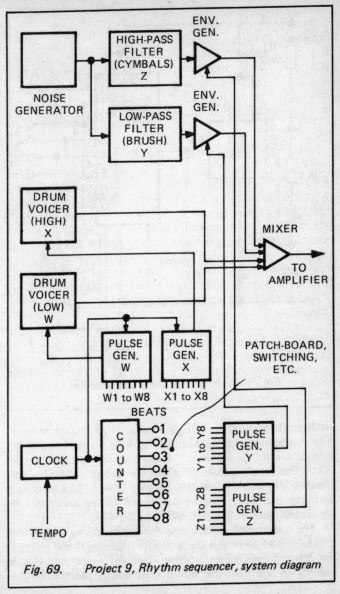

Fig. 69.   Project 9, Rhythm sequencer, system diagram

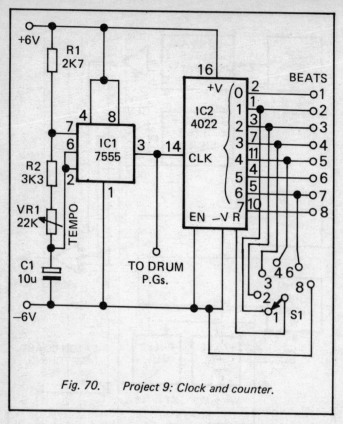

Fig. 70.   Project 9: Clock and counter.

or bar. The output of the clock goes to an 8-stage counter. The outputs of this are normally at logical low, but go high one at a time, in sequence. These give the beats within the bar. The rotary switch S1 allows the counter to be reset to shorten the sequence, so that we may have 1, 2, 3, 4, 6 or 8 beats to the bar. Thus we can obtain all the common time signatures, such as 2/4, 3/4, 6/8 and others.

The noise-based sounds are produced by taking the random 'white noise' from a noise generator, filtering it and giving it an envelope. Figure 71 shows that the noise generator is simply an npn transistor with its base-emitter junction reverse-

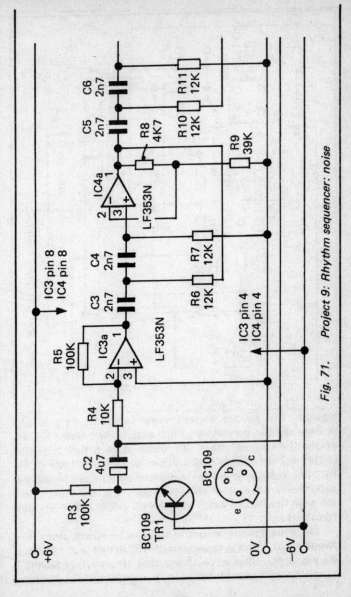

Fig. 71. Project 9: Rhythm sequencer: noise

123

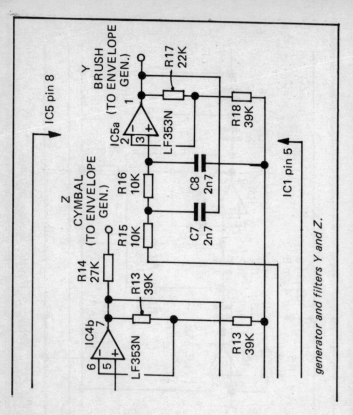

generator and filters Y and Z.

biased. The leakage current varies erratically in a totally random manner, generating a fluctuating voltage across R3. To obtain the cymbal effect, the white noise is first amplified (IC3a) and then filtered by a 4th-order high-pass filter (IC4a, b). The filtering is further enhanced by R14 in conjunction with the capacitance of the next stage. For the brush effect we send the white noise directly to a 2nd order low-pass filter (IC5a).

Drum sounds are made by using a band-pass filter as a *voicer* (Fig. 72). Comparison with Figures 43 and 55 reveals that this circuit has a twin-T rejection network in its feedback loop. As in Figure 43, feedback is negative since any increase

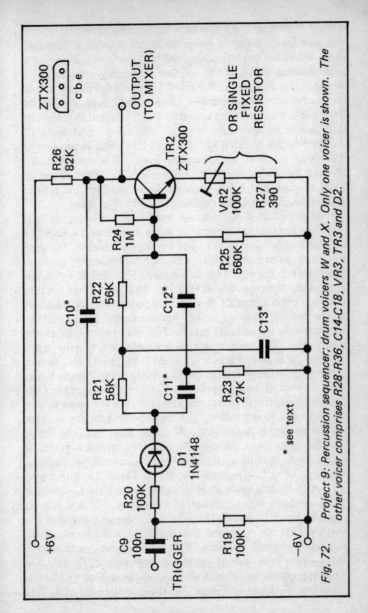

Fig. 72. Project 9: Percussion sequencer; drum voicers W and X. Only one voicer is shown. The other voicer comprises R28-R36, C14-C18, VR3, TR3 and D2.

125

in base current to TR2 results in an increase in collector current and hence a *fall* in potential at the junction of R26 and C10. When the circuit is triggered by a positive-going pulse a brief damped signal at the selected frequency appears at its output. The frequency is selected by choosing suitable values for the resistors and capacitors of the twin-T network and the feedback capacitor. R21 and R22 must be equal in value and R23 should be approximately half this value. C11 and C12 should be equal in value with C10 and C13 being about double this value. Values are discussed later. The sound is also affected by the value of the resistors in the emitter circuit of TR2, as explained later. Because the voicer circuit is a filter with relatively low Q the oscillations die away quickly.

The noise-based sounds are produced continuously and therefore require an envelope to shape them into the sound of a cymbal or brushed drum. The envelope is obtained by using a transconductance amplifier (Fig.73) controlled by an envelope shaping circuit. This is triggered into action by pulses originating from the counter (Fig.70). In Figure 73 we see that there are eight inputs Z1 to Z8 which may be connected either to the counter outputs or left unconnected. Those that are connected to the counter receive a positive-going pulse on the beat. The NOR gate produces a negative-going pulse when any one (or more) of inputs Z1 to Z8 is triggered. This in turn triggers the pulse-generator (IC7). As its output at pin 3 goes high, current flows through D3, charging the capacitor C28. The rising potential causes the amplifier (IC8) to begin to pass filtered noise to the mixer. The envelope rises rapidly simulating the striking of the cymbal. When the pulse ends, the charge on C28 leaks away through D4 and R46, giving a moderate decay time. A similar circuit is used for controlling the brush sound. The circuit is similar to that in Figure 73, with inputs Y1 to Y8 leading through 39nF capacitors C27 to C34 to IC9, which replaces IC6 of Figure 73. Similarly, IC7 and IC8 are replaced by IC10 and IC11. The difference in Generator Y is that its envelope rises and falls rapidly, so the length of the pulse is shortened by using 1MΩ as timing resistor (replacing R45) and 47n as timing capacitor (replacing C27). Also, the envelope generator is reduced to a single resistor (R58) and capacitor (C38) as in Figure 74; these replace D3, D4, R46

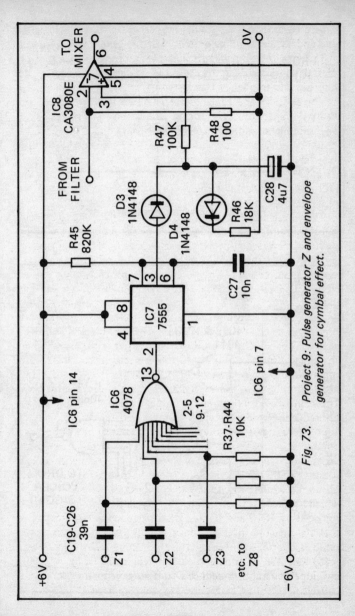

Fig. 73. Project 9: Pulse generator Z and envelope generator for cymbal effect.

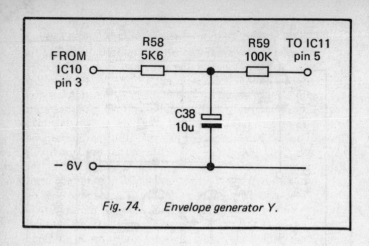

Fig. 74.   Envelope generator Y.

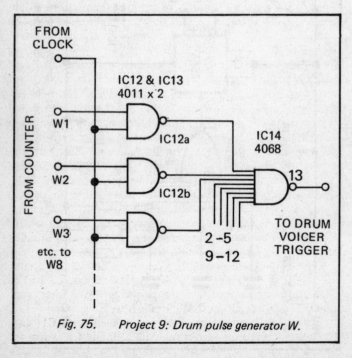

Fig. 75.   Project 9: Drum pulse generator W.

128

and C28 of Figure 73.

The filter-based sounds are triggered by the logical network of Figure 75. The inputs W1 to W8 are connected either to the counter or to 0V. Whereas the circuit of Figure 73 is *edge-sensitive*, because of the capacitors C19 to C26, the circuit of Figure 75 is *level-sensitive*. The problem is that if A1 is connected to, say, output 1 of the counter and W2 is connected to output 2, there is no gap between 1 going low and 2 going high. The circuit would register only the first beat, not the second. In Figure 75 we NAND the outputs from the counter with the signal from the clock. Figure 76 explains the section.

The noise-based and filter-based sounds are combined into a single audio signal by a mixer (Fig.77). The variable resistors allow the relative volume of each component of the signal to be controlled. Note that, since the signal from the filters has a naturally sharp attack and decay, there is no need for an envelope-shaper. The output from this mixer may then be fed to an amplifier such as one of those shown in Figures 61 and 67.

Variations

The system diagram of Figure 69 shows two noise-based and two filter-based sources of sound, but there is no need to incorporate all of these. Conversely, the system can easily be extended to include an even wider range of sound sources of both types. It is possible to simplify the triggering circuit by using a gate with fewer inputs in place of IC6 (and IC9). The 4075 4-input NOR gate or the 4023 3-input NOR gate are suitable. Similarly a 4-input NAND gate (4012) or 3-input NAND gate (4023) can be used in Figure 75. Indeed if only two beats per bar are required, a single 4011 IC can be used to replace IC12 and IC14 (also IC15 and IC17).

There is much scope for experimentation to find which combination of component values gives the required sounds. Here are some suggestions worth trying:

Figure 71, Noise filters: The capacitors shown give a cut-off point of 6kHz for both filters. Try varying C3 to C6 (keeping them all equal) to change the high-pass filter, and vary C7 and C8 to change the low-pass filter.

Figure 72, Drum voicers: For a low-pitched drum, C11 and C12 can be 100nF or even more, with C10 and C13 equal to

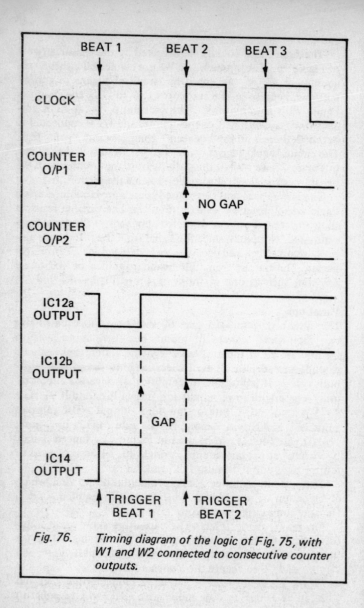

Fig. 76.   Timing diagram of the logic of Fig. 75, with
            W1 and W2 connected to consecutive counter
            outputs.

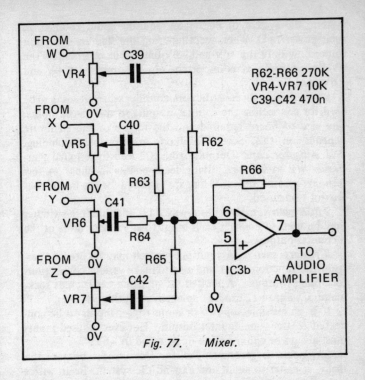

Fig. 77.   Mixer.

220nF, the resistors having the values shown in Figure 72. For a high-pitched maracas effect, C11 and C12 are 4.7nF and C10 and C13 are 10nF. If R27 and VR2 are to be replaced by a fixed resistor, one of 100kΩ is generally suitable for a low-pitched drum, while a resistor of about 390Ω produces a sharper sound.

Figure 73, Envelope generators: Vary pulse length by changing R45 and C27. Vary attack by inserting a resistor of a few tens of kilohms between pin 3 of IC7 and D3. Vary the decay period by replacing R46. **IMPORTANT: do not vary R47; reducing this can destroy IC8.**

Construction

The project requires a dual ±6V supply; two 6V batteries are suitable. The current required depends on the size of the

131

system, the system of Figure 69 requiring about 180mA, on each power rail. When working from the figures, note that some show only the +6V and −6V lines while others show the 0V line as well. It is important not to confuse the 0V and −6V lines.

Before beginning construction, consider what means is to be used for connecting the counter outputs to the trigger inputs. The size of board required and the nature of the enclosure depends on this. Several methods are possible, including,

1 Alligator clips: Outputs from IC2 lead to terminal pins. Inputs W1 to Z8 have flying leads ending in clips. A few terminal pins on the −6V line are provided for the inputs that are not being used.

2 PCB switches: Banks of 8-way d.i.l. subminiature switches may be used to connect each input to any one or more of the 8 counter outputs.

3 Rotary switch: A multipole switch may be used to perform the function of S1 and also to make various connections to counter outputs. A limited set of sequences such as rock, mambo, waltz, etc., can be implemented in this way.

It is permissible for two or more trigger inputs to be connected to the same counter output. However, unused inputs must always be connected to or switched to −6V.

Stripboard is recommended for this project because this makes it easier to adapt and expand the system. Begin with a rather larger board than you think you will eventually need, as it is almost inevitable that you will want to add more sounds later.

If you do not have an audio amplifier available, build one using the circuits of Figures 61 or 67. Next build the noise generator and its amplifier (IC3a). The circuit diagrams are based on using the LF353 dual FET op amp but, if you prefer, you can use the single version, the LF351. You could consider using the quad version, the LF347, but this may result in having to crowd rather too many resistors and capacitors around the IC, making it difficult to change things later. It will probably be necessary to try several transistors for TR1 before you find one that produces a sufficient volume of noise. A BC109 is shown in Figure 71 but any other type of npn transistor can be used. With an especially noisy transistor, IC3a may have too high a gain, in which case reduce the value of R5. At this stage the output from IC3a may be connected directly to the input of the audio amplifier that you intend to use. To complete this section of the system, build the high-pass and low-pass filters (IC4 and IC5a), possibly with different capacitor values (see above).

Next build the clock and counter; the rotary switch allows for all the usual time signatures but, if you will never require anything but 8 beats to the bar, omit S1 and wire pin 4 pin 15 directly to −6V.

The control circuit for the envelope generators is the next stage to be constructed. Notes on the selection of component values have been given above. The outputs from these envelope circuits are wired to the mixer and the signal from this goes to the audio amplifier. At this stage the sequencer can be tested, using only noise-based sounds.

The drum pulse generator and drum voicers complete the system, and are wired directly to the mixer. The whole system can now be tested. Depending on the layout you adopt, it may be necessary to add a few capacitors to the circuit to smooth out 'spikes' on the supply line, particularly near the logic ICs. These may cause unwanted noise and oscillations. Use 100nF polyester capacitors in the area of the board where IC2 and IC12−IC14 are situated. Solder one wire of the capacitor to the +6V line and the other to the −6V line. You may also need a 100μF electrolytic capacitor soldered as close as possible to pins 1 and 8 of IC1.

Using the System

The sequencer can produce any sequence of effects, working on a bar length of up to 8 beats. Although the variety of possible sequences is enormous, here are a few suggestions for obtaining some popular rhythms, showing which counter outputs to use:

Swing: 4/4 time, 8 quavers to the bar, S1 to 8; cymbal to 1, 3, 4, 5, 7, 8; drum to 1, 3, 5, 7.

Rock: 4/4 time, 8 quavers to the bar; S1 to 8; cymbal to 1, 2, 3, 4, 5, 6, 7, 8; drum to 3, 7; bass drum to 1, 4 (optional).

Modern Waltz: 3/4 time, 3 crotchets to the bar, S1 to 3; drum to 1; hi-hat high-pitched cymbal to 2, 3.

Latin American: 4/4 time, 8 quavers to the bar, S1 to 8; drum to 1, 4, 7; hi-hat to 2, 3, 5, 6. This is the basic habanera rhythm, and can be played without the hi-hat accompaniment.

Samba: 2/4 time, 8 semi-quavers to the bar; small drum to 1, 4, 5, 6, 8; large drum to 1, 5; hi-hat to 1, 5, 7 or to 1, 3, 4, 5, 7. The bossa nova is the same rhythm, played more slowly.

Special Components

Resistors are all 0.25W carbon or metal film; 5% tolerance is adequate for all, including those used in the filters.

Capacitors are electrolytic or polyester, as indicated in the diagrams.

Integrated Circuits

IC1, IC7 & IC10	7555 CMOS timer
IC2	4022 CMOS divide-by-8 counter with 1-of-8 outputs
IC3–IC5	LF355N dual operational amplifier with JFET inputs
IC6, IC9	4078 CMOS 8-input NOR gate
IC8, IC11	CA3080E operational transconductance amplifier
IC12, IC13, IC15, IC16	4011 CMOS quadruple 2-input NAND gate
IC14, IC17	4068 CMOS 8-input NAND gate

PROJECT 10 – Electronic Organ *Levels 2 and 3*

This is a complete organ project which, in its simpler versions, has a range of up to 5 octaves (61 keys) and has a formant filter and envelope-shaper to imitate one or more of a range of musical instruments. The project is based on a relatively inexpensive organ chip and configures it for use as a solo instrument. It can play single notes or chords and the circuit may be set to sound the note for as long as the key is held down (sustain off) or to continue the note until the next note is played (sustain on). The organ IC has several other facilities not made use of in this project, but which can be incorporated at a later date to produce a sophisticated keyboard instrument. These include the ability to split the keyboard into two sections to play solo and accompaniment, and a number of options for automatic chording. To implement the full range of features the reader is referred to the manufacturer's data sheet.

Since this project relies on only the more basic features of the chip, it should prove possible to adapt the design to use other similar organ chips instead.

How It Works

This organ is based on digital electronics. Compare this with Project 11 in which pitch depends on an analogue voltage. In this project the frequency of a clock (1.00012MHz) is divided repeatedly to produce any note in the range from three octaves below middle C (32Hz) to 4 octaves above it (4186 Hz). The frequency or frequencies played at any moment depend on the result of automatic scanning of the keyboard. Each of outputs B1 to B6 (Fig. 78) are normally high but go briefly low in turn. These correspond to the 5 octaves of the instrument and a number of function keys. Each output is connected through a diode and a normally-open switch to 12 inputs F1 to F12, one for each note of the chromatic steps of an octave. If any one or more of these keys is pressed (closed) at the instant the low pulse appears on the B output, the note(s) in that octave is sounded. The output signal appears at 3 different outputs, known as the *footages*. These are one octave apart so that the 8′ output has half the frequency of the 4′ output and the 16′ output has half the

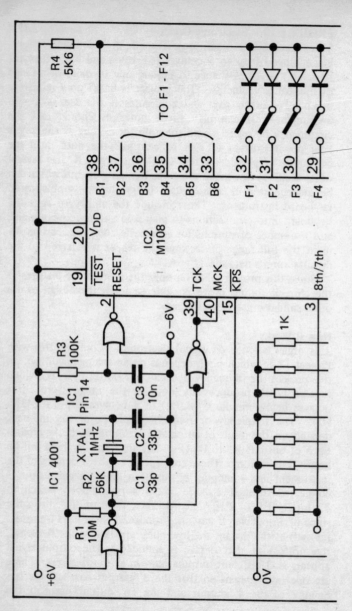

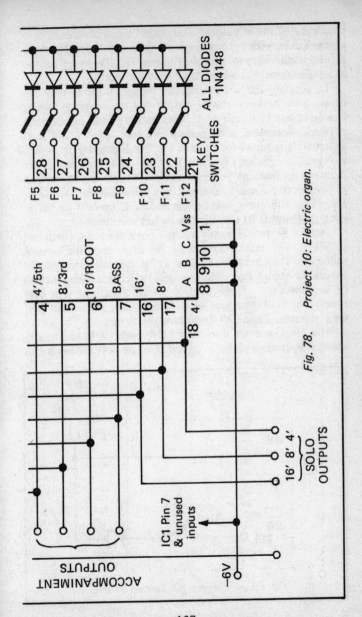

Fig. 78.   Project 10: Electric organ.

137

frequency of the 8′ output. The output signal consists of true square waves, with 1:1 mark/space ratio (page 100). There are 5 other audio outputs shown in Figure 78. These are for the accompaniment, but are not used in this project.

To simplify the circuit diagram, Figure 78 shows only the connections between the B1 output and the twelve F inputs. If a complete keyboard of 61 keys is to be used, an identical network, complete with pull-up resistors, diodes and key-switches, is required for each of the five B outputs, B1 to B5. However, a smaller keyboard may be used, covering fewer octaves. In this case you may decide to omit the lowest one or two octaves, and to connect key networks only to B3 to B5. This will cover notes from middle C upward on the 8′ output. Outputs B1 and B2 may be left unconnected.

Output B6 provides only a single note, the top C (switched to F1). The main function of B6 is to scan the control switches. The circuit is the same as for the other B outputs in Figure 78 except that slide or toggle switches are used instead of key-switches. These control several functions (see data sheet) but in this project we need only one, the sustain ON/OFF selector. Figure 79 shows how this is wired.

The clock is built from two NOR gates (IC1) and its frequency is controlled by a crystal. For greatest precision this

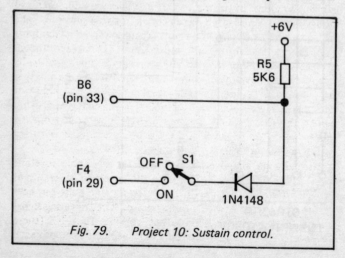

Fig. 79.   *Project 10: Sustain control.*

should be a 1.00012MHz crystal, but the more easily obtained 1MHz crystal is good enough. A third gate in IC1 is used to give a short high pulse to reset the organ chip whenever power is switched on.

Format Filtering

The square-wave output signal can be fed directly to an amplifier such as that in Figure 61 or Figure 67. This gives a reasonably pleasant 'organ' tone suitable for practising. For more interesting effects the signal is filtered. For greatest flexibility, build the tunable audio filter (Project 4), either as a separate unit, or on the same board as the organ. With its range of LP, HP and BP outputs it enables a wide variety of sounds to be produced. If you require only one or a few sounds, build fixed active filters for each effect, as described in Chapter 11. Project 4, if available, is used in the initial stages to investigate the possibilities and decide on cut-off points.

As explained on page 110, sounds obtained by filtering a square wave are usually imperfect, owing to the lack of the even harmonics. However, it is still worth experimenting with the square-wave output, especially by using an amplitude envelope, as explained later. Fortunately, the even harmonics can be obtained in this project by mixing two adjacent footages. Figure 80 shows a mixer circuit for this purpose. The signals from the 8' and 4' outputs are mixed in equal amounts by feeding them to inputs A and B, input C being left unconnected. For certain instruments we require one signal to be stronger than the other. One is connected to A (the stronger one) and one to input C (the weaker one). The values of resistors in Figure 80 are possibly subject to changes, depending on the exact sound required. The connections from the footage outputs to A, B and C could be made by a rotary switch, wired for different instrumental effects.

Virtually no sound is realistic without a suitable envelope (page 111). In this project we use the envelope generator of Project 8 (Fig. 67). This is triggered by a rising pulse but here we need to trigger it with a falling pulse. The triggering signal is the $\overline{\text{KPS}}$ (key pressed solo) output from pin 15 of IC2 (there are several other similar outputs not used in this project).

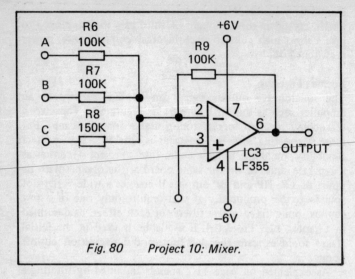

Fig. 80   Project 10: Mixer.

This output is normally high but goes low for as long as any
key is pressed and held. The low-going signal turns on the pnp
transistor (Fig. 81), causing the voltage at its collector to rise.
This starts the attack phase. The sustain phase lasts for as
long as the key is held. The decay phase begins when the key
is released. In order that the note is heard during the decay
phase, S1 must be switched to 'sustain ON' whenever the
envelope generator is in use.

Construction
The circuit requires 75mA on each power rail to operate the
complete system, including the audio amplifier, tunable filter
and envelope generator. It can be powered by a pair of 6V
batteries or by a dual ±6V power pack.

Keyboards with piano-type keys may be purchased ready-
made, either with 61 keys or in a cheaper version with only 49
keys. Keyboards are sold without any supporting frame so it
is necessary to build a 'box' of some kind. This may also hold
the circuit board and power supply. The loudspeaker and
control switches are mounted on top of the box. As with
several of the projects in this book, there is much scope for

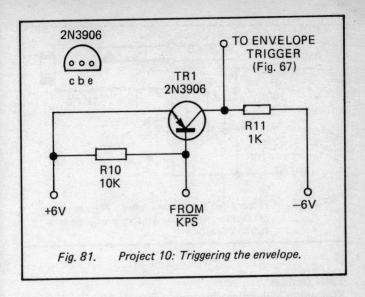

Fig. 81. *Project 10: Triggering the envelope.*

expansion, so leave plenty of room in the box for additional circuit boards and on top of the box for extra control switches. You may at some time wish to include the Percussion Sequencer (Project 9).

In the initial stages the expense of a piano-type keyboard may be avoided by using a calculator keypad. These are available very cheaply with 12 or more push-buttons. Although they are far less easily playable than a proper keyboard, some fun may be had using such a keypad. However, keypads usually have a certain amount of internal wiring which means that the keys are not individually accessible. This may make it impossible to use the pad with this project, so check the connecting matrix of the pad before purchasing it.

The output from the audio amplifier will normally go to a loudspeaker, but it is useful to provide a socket so that the user may use earphones instead. A jack socket is wired as in Figure 82 so that inserting the earphone plug disconnects the loudspeaker.

141

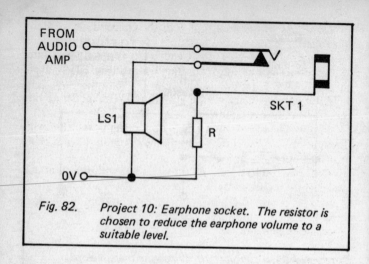

Fig. 82. *Project 10: Earphone socket. The resistor is chosen to reduce the earphone volume to a suitable level.*

Filter Options

The matter of deciding what type of filter or filters are required is left to the preferences of the constructor. These are very many possibilities, which are best tried out in advance on a breadboard. Below are some suggested starting points, all of which are made on the basis of a state-variable filter as in Figure 51. If only a single effect is required, the variable resistors may be replaced by fixed resistors and the switched capacitors by single capacitors. Alternatively use a 2nd-order active filter (or a pair of such filters for band-pass filtering) as described in Chapter 11. Similarly, the circuit of the envelope generator may be simplified by substituting fixed resistors for the variable ones.

Piano: Connect 4′ and 8′ outputs to A and B (Fig. 80). Low-pass filter with cut-off about 20kHz, high Q. Rapid attack, slow decay.

Organ (open diapason): Connect 4′ and 8′ to A and B. Low-pass filter with cut-off about 2kHz. Fairly rapid attack and decay.

Clarinet: Connect 4′ to C and 8′ to A. Low-pass filter with cut-off about 10kHz. Rapid (almost maximum) attack and decay.

Oboe: As for clarinet, but with the connections to A and C reversed.

Trumpet: Connect 4′ to A and 8′ to C. Band-pass filter with cut-off about 10kHz. Rapid attack and fairly rapid decay.

Horn: As for trumpet with cut-off at 1kHz, moderate rate of attack and more rapid decay.

Violin: Connect 4′ to A and 8′ to C. High-pass filter with low cut-off, about 1kHz or even a few hundred hertz. Slow attack, moderately fast decay.

Cello and Double-bass: As for violin but with slower attack and slightly slower decay.

Special Components

Integrated Circuits

IC1	4001 CMOS quadruple 2-input NOR gate
IC2	M108 single chip organ (solo + accompaniment); an alternative is the M208 which differs only in the split of the keyboard in accompaniment mode.

Chapter 9

VOLTAGE-CONTROLLED FILTERS

There are many occasions when it is useful to be able to control the cut-off point of a filter by electronic means, rather than by adjusting one or more variable resistors. The most direct way of doing this is to employ the equivalent of electronically variable resistors in the filter circuit. A control voltage alters the effective value of the 'resistor' and so changes the response of the filter.

A device that has the properties of an electronically controlled resistor is the transconductance amplifier. We have already used this in the envelope generator circuits of Project 9 (Fig. 73). The amplifier produces a *current*, the size of which is proportional to the difference in *voltage* between its input terminals. This is analogous to a resistor, since the size of the current passing through a resistor is likewise proportional to the difference in voltage between its two ends. The ratio voltage/current for a resistor is its *resistance*, while the inverse ratio, current/voltage, is its *conductance.* Similarly the ratio current/voltage for the amplifier is its *transconductance, g_m*. The value of g_m is determined by a voltage applied to the control input of the amplifier.

Transconductance amplifiers can be used in most types of filter to replace the frequency-determining resistor or resistors. Several amplifiers, all controlled by the same voltage level, can be used to replace ganged variable resistors in multi-stage filters. The project at the end of this chapter shows how a pair of transconductance amplifiers are used in a state-variable filter (Fig. 83). The circuit is essentially the same as that of Figure 48, except that the resistors linking the summer to the first integrator and the first integrator to the second integrator are each replaced by a transconductance amplifier. These are the equivalent of the ganged variable resistors VR2 and VR3 of the practical filter of Figure 51. The filter of Figure 83 also differs in that the resistors between the 0V rail and the (+) inputs of the op amps are omitted, but this is only because they are an unnecessary refinement for this particular project.

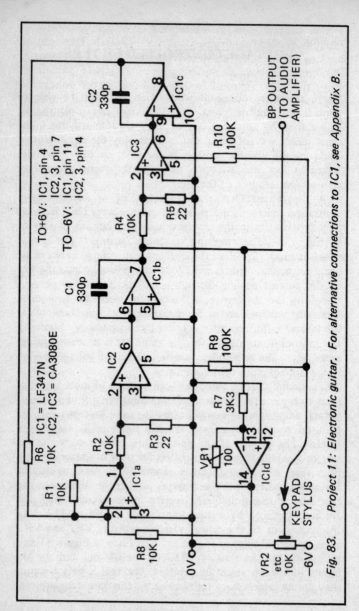

Fig. 83. Project 11: Electronic guitar. For alternative connections to IC1, see Appendix B.

IC1 = LF347N
IC2, IC3 = CA3080E

TO +6V: IC1, pin 4
IC2, 3, pin 7
TO −6V: IC1, pin 11
IC2, 3, pin 4

BP OUTPUT (TO AUDIO AMPLIFIER)

One popular field for the application of voltage-controlled filters is in electronic organs and synthesisers. They can be used to enhance the realism of certain sounds. For example, the sound of a cymbal contains more of the higher frequencies when it is first struck. By lowering the cut-off point of a voltage-controlled low-pass filter while the cymbal is sounding, an overall fall in the average pitch of the white noise can be obtained. A similar technique is used when simulating brass instruments, to filter out the higher frequencies after the attack phase is over.

In electronic synthesisers, voltage-controlled filters are used to produce sounds unlike those produced by normal musical instruments. In most instruments the spectrum is strongly influenced by resonances at a number of fixed frequencies. This is the basis of *formant filtering* described in the previous chapter. If, instead of a fixed filter, we use one in which the cut-off point varies with the pitch of the note being played, the apparent resonances shift and we obtain a sound which has a distinctly different quality.

PROJECT 11 – Electronic Guitar   *Level 1*

This is an inexpensive and easily constructed fun project, to amuse the younger members of the family. It produces a sound very similar to a plucked string, which is why it is called a 'guitar'. The nature of the sound varies slightly depending on exactly how the board is laid out and upon the pitch of the note. In its higher registers its sound is more reminiscent of the Indian instrument, the sitar.

Without the keyboard section (VR2, etc.), with the addition of a 10kΩ input resistor connected to pin 2 of IC1a, and with a 10kΩ variable resistor for VR1, this circuit functions as a straightforward voltage-controlled filter. The values of C1 and C2 may be altered to make it operate over a different range of frequencies.

How It Works

The circuit (Fig. 83) is essentially a state-variable filter based on four operational amplifiers all contained in a single IC. It also has a pair of transconductance amplifiers to act as voltage-controlled resistors, as explained on page 146. The inverter amplifier (IC1d, compare with Fig. 48) has a low-value feedback resistor, VR1, so that the damping signal it sends to the summer amplifier (IC1a) is much attenuated. The result is that the filter has low damping or, conversely, high Q (page 74). Any electrical stimulation of the circuit sets the filter oscillating for a length of time depending on the setting of VR1. In use, VR1 is set so that the filter oscillates for a second or so, the oscillations gradually dying away in the same way as those on a plucked string.

The damping signal is taken from the band-pass output so that the frequency of oscillation depends on the centre-frequency of the filter. This is controlled by the voltage applied to the transconductance amplifiers. The higher the voltage, the higher the pitch of the note. The voltage for each note is obtained from a series of variable resistors, of which only one (VR2) is shown in Figure 83. From the wiper of each resistor a wire leads to a keypad. This can be one of a number of copper pads etched on a PCB to resemble the keyboard of a piano. Or it could just be a row of drawing-pins (thumb-tacks) pressed into a strip of wood or strip of plastic. The stylus is touched briefly against one of the key-pads. This sets the control voltage and at the same time stimulates the circuit into oscillation. The signal from the band-pass output goes to an audio amplifier (see Fig. 61 or Fig. 67).

Construction
The project is suitable for battery-power, two 6V batteries or battery holders each with 4 AA cells being required. It may be built on a single piece of stripboard, but leave enough room around IC1 to allow for the wiring, resistors and capacitors associated with that IC. As explained earlier, the 'keyboard' can take a number of forms. If stripboard is being used, the ends of the strips can be used as keypads. The stylus is a 4mm wander plug on the end of a flexible lead. The number of notes provided can range between 8 (an octave with no sharps or flats) and 24 (two octaves including sharps and flats). If a high-gain audio amplifier is used (e.g. Fig. 61) it may be

necessary to wire a resistor of up to 3.3MΩ between the BP output and the amplifier input.

Setting up the circuit requires careful adjustment of VR1. If VR1 is set to too high a value, the sound is damped out quickly, giving a pizzicato effect. If VR1 is set too low the circuit goes into continuous oscillation. Set VR1 so that the circuit oscillates for a second or two when the stylus is touched to a keypad.

Special Components

Capacitors
C1, C2   330pF polystyrene

Integrated Circuits
IC1   LF347 quadruple JFET op amp
IC2, IC3   CA3080E transconductance amplifiers

Chapter 10

DIGITAL FILTERING

The filters previously described in this book have all dealt with continuously variable quantities — voltages or currents that can have any value within a given range. This is the result of the nature of the components, the resistors, capacitors and amplifiers used in building them. Such filters are referred to as *analogue filters*. In this chapter we look at filters based on digital electronics. In these we are mainly concerned with logic levels, voltages which may be high or low, but are not allowed to take values in between.

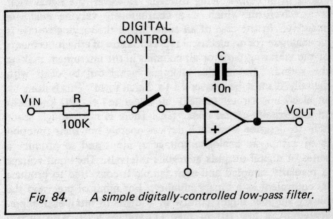

Fig. 84. A simple digitally-controlled low-pass filter.

Before we go on to discuss digital filters we must mention another category of filter that is sometimes referred to as digital or, more accurately, *digitally-controlled*. Figure 84 shows a simple low-pass filter of this kind. The filter works by gradually accumulating charge on the capacitor or gradually losing charge from the capacitor, in the same way as any other active filter. But the filter has a switch that can be turned on or off at high frequency by digital means. If the switch is permanently closed, the circuit behaves as a filter with cut-off point at 160Hz. This is calculated from the equation

$f = 1/2\pi RC$, with R having the value 100kΩ. If we apply a square wave (i.e. digital) signal to the gate which controls the switch, we can arrange to turn the switch on and off at high speed. Suppose that this signal turns the switch on for exactly half of the time. The resistor now conducts for only half the time and consequently passes only half the amount of charge. It becomes equivalent to a 200kΩ resistor, and the cut-off frequency is reduced to 80Hz. By varying the proportion of time for which the switch is closed we can vary the cut-off frequency of the filter. However, although the filter is controlled by digital means the actual filtering is still done by a resistor and a capacitor. This puts it in the same category as the switched capacitor filters described in Chapter 7.

In true digital filtering the signal itself is converted to digital form *before* being filtered. However, the signal itself is a waveform which is a continuously varying *analogue* quantity. In the case of an audio signal the varying voltage is an analogue (or an electrical representation of) the movements of the vibrating parts or air columns in the instrument making the sound. Before this analogue signal can be dealt with digitally it must be converted to digital form. This is done by an electronic circuit (usually an integrated circuit) known as an *analogue-to-digital converter.* There is not enough space here to describe how such devices operate but their function is to accept an analogue voltage as input and to produce a series of digital outputs at regular intervals. The input voltage is regularly sampled and each sample is converted to produce its equivalent as a binary number. For minimal precision the binary number might consist of 8 digits (8 bits), each represented by a low (0) or high (1) voltage level. With such a converter the analogue input may range between 0V and (for example) 2.55V, and take any of an infinite number of different values within that range. The output has only 256 possible values, ranging from zero (binary 00000000) to 255 (binary 11111111). Figure 85 shows the result of sampling a sine wave and converting it to an 8-bit output. It is the limited number of output values that causes loss of precision. A-to-D converters with 8-bit resolution are available cheaply but for higher resolution it is commonplace to employ converters with as many as 12 or 16 bits in their output. A 16-bit output has

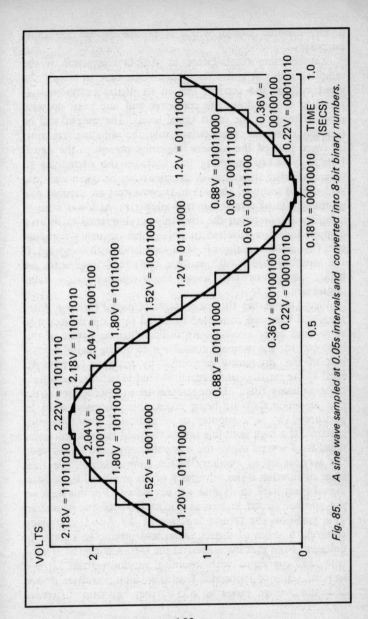

Fig. 85. A sine wave sampled at 0.05s intervals and converted into 8-bit binary numbers.

65536 possible values, which is precise enough for most purposes.

Another important factor in A-to-D conversion is the sampling rate. A converter takes a finite time to sample the input voltage and convert this to its digital equivalent. If sampling is too slow, the converter will not keep up with rapid changes in the input signal level. The output will be seriously distorted. As a general rule, the sampling rate must be twice that of the highest frequency present in the signal. For high-fidelity sampling this includes the harmonics so several tens of thousands of samples must be taken and converted each second. Many A-to-D converters are capable of a sampling rate of several hundred kilohertz. At lower rates of sampling the fact that the smoothly varying signal takes on a stepped form is equivalent to adding high-frequency components (the *sudden* changes in level associated with stepping). If the sampling rate is high enough, the added frequencies are higher and come well above the frequency range being considered.

Figure 86 shows the main stages of digital filtering. After the signal has been converted to digital form it is subjected to some kind of processing. We shall discuss the nature of this later but for the moment consider it to be the digital equivalent of the 'processing' performed by analogue components such as the resistors and capacitors (and sometimes inductors) of an ordinary filter. If the samples are to be processed at the rate at which they are being taken, this processing must be performed by a computer or a dedicated microprocessor system. If a high sampling rate is required and the processing consists of several stages the computer may need to call upon the services of an auxiliary maths co-processor. The final stage of filtering is the conversion of the processed signal from digital form back to its analogue equivalent. For this stage we use another circuit known as a *digital-to-analogue converter*. This performs the reverse function of the A-to-D converter, receiving a series of digital values and producing a *series* of voltages. Note that the output of the D-to-A converter is not a true analogue signal with smoothly varying voltage. It is a *stepped* series of voltages. Thus if an 8-bit converter is used and the voltage range is 2.55V, the minimum difference

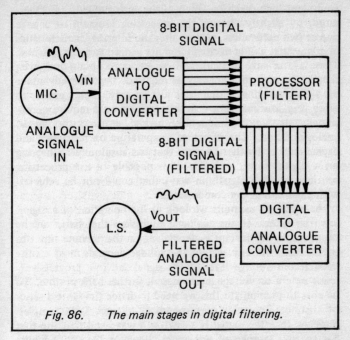

Fig. 86.   The main stages in digital filtering.

between one step and the adjacent step is 0.01V. This again leads to loss of resolution and the introduction of high-frequency components into the output signal. This may be made of less importance by using a 12-bit or 16-bit converter and by using a high sampling rate. An active low-pass resistor-capacitor filter may also be used to remove the high-frequency components from the output signal.

Signal Processing

Processing the digitised signal is a mathematical operation which can be as elaborate as we like and can be performed with any required degree of precision. This means that the expense of high-precision resistors and capacitors is avoided, even supposing that components of the required values are actually obtainable. In digital filtering a few mathematical steps can replace several stages of resistor-capacitor filtering. These two factors tend to make digital filters cheaper than the equivalent high-precision filters of the analogue kind. Furthermore, by slightly altering the processing program to change one or two parameters, we can alter the filtering characteristics in a way that would normally require ganged variable resistors. These are usually difficult and expensive to obtain and, even then, may not work entirely as required. Another advantage of digital filtering is that it is just as easy, if not easier, to filter very low frequency signals which would require exceptionally or almost impossibly high-value capacitors in an analogue filter. The effect of temperature on resistance and capacitance is another bugbear that has absolutely no bearing on a digital filter. Finally, it is possible to use processing routines to filter signals in ways that could not be achieved with passive or active components.

As a simple example we look at the operation of a digital low-pass filter. In the analogue equivalent the charge on the capacitor at any instant is dependent on the previous input to the circuit. At any instant the voltage depends most on the most recent voltage level of the signal and to a progressively lesser extent on voltage levels present further back in time. To be able to manipulate this we need to divide time into a series of distinct intervals, corresponding to successive samples. Suppose that the signal is a sawtooth wave and that the first 5 successive samples of this are as shown on the left of Figure 87(a). The sampling rate shown here is too low to be of use in a practical filter but having only a few samples makes the calculations easier to understand.

We can now define the characteristics of a particular digital filter by saying that, at each sampling time the signal value (corresponding to the charge on the capacitor) is equal to the current sample, plus half of the previous sample, plus a quarter of the previous sample, plus an eighth of the previous sample, plus one-sixteenth of the previous sample. Samples earlier than these are to be ignored.

Thus at time t_4 the signal value is:

$$t_4 + t_3/2 + t_2/4 + t_1/8 + t_0/16 .$$

Putting in the values of these five samples, their total is:

$$0.2 + 0.15/2 + 0.1/4 + 0.05/8 + 0/16 = 0.30625$$

This is the first point plotted on the graph of Figure 87(b). The next point, at t_5, is calculated in a similar way, but based on values at t_1 to t_5. This process is repeated for each time point, always basing the value on the current value and the previous four signal values. When this is done and the points are joined, the resulting curve (the output signal) takes the form shown. The sawtooth shape is still obvious, but its 'sharp points' are rounded off. In other words, the more rapid changes of level have been reduced; the higher frequencies have been 'filtered' out. This is a low-pass filter.

The calculation described above produces one sort of low-pass filter with a particular cut-off point. By varying the routine in different ways it is possible to produce other low-pass filters. For example, we could increase or reduce the number of recent samples taken into account. Or we could have a different series of divisors, for example:

$$t_4 + t_3/3 + t_2/6 + t_1/9 + t_0/12 .$$

Without becoming involved in building the hardware, it is interesting to write short computer programs (as was done for the graphs of Fig. 87) to investigate the effects of such routines on a given input signal.

Other routines can readily be devised and programmed for performing other types of filtering. One feature of a routine may be to take the output of the first stages of the calculation and add a portion of this into the second stage of the calculation. This is the equivalent of using feedback, as we do when using operational amplifiers in active filters. With a little mathematical know-how it is possible to program low-pass, band-pass and high-pass filters of all the well-known types, such as Butterworth, Chebyshev and others. With a little more expertise it is possible to produce filters of a variety of bizarre and otherwise unrealisable types.

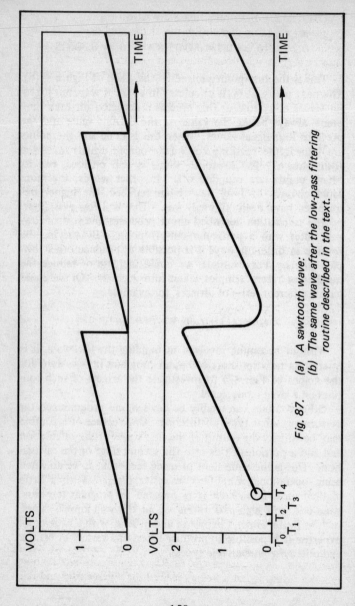

Fig. 87. (a) A sawtooth wave:
(b) The same wave after the low-pass filtering
routine described in the text.

158

PROJECT 12 – Discriminating Baby Alarm   *Level 2*

A project based on digital filtering of the kind described above would not only be higher than 'level 3' but would need an interface to a microcomputer and require the reader to be familiar with programming in assembler. Instead, recalling the remarks made earlier in the chapter about digital filters being able to operate on very low frequency signals, this project is a rather specialised type of filter. As with Project 1, its function is to filter out unwanted signals.

If we consider the sounds likely to be heard whilst baby is supposed to be asleep, there are two main types:

(1)   Short-period sounds; sporadic contented snuffles, an occasional sneeze or hiccup, the sound of baby's hand striking the cothead as he or she turns over, the sound of a door slamming or the window rattling (this door may be the door of another room, but it may nevertheless be picked up by the microphone beside the cot), the sound of passing traffic, and other transitory and unimportant sounds.

(2)   Long-period sounds: baby wakes up and begins to babble, shout or cry. Baby needs attention!

The purpose of this project is to discriminate between these two types of sound, to ignore the first and to call the baby-minder's attention to the second.

How It Works

The basic quantity with which this circuit deals is the *presence* or *absence* of sound. The timbre or frequency of the sound is not taken into account. Presence or absence of sound is a binary quantity – there either *is* sound or there *is not*. Because of the binary (and therefore digital) nature of the sound, no A-to-D converter is necessary in this system. All that is required is a sound detector with a binary (sound/no-sound) output. Sound is detected by the crystal microphone (XTAL1, Fig. 88), the sound signal being amplified by TR1 and the Darlington transistor TR2. When there is no sound the voltage at the upper end of R5 remains constant at about +2.5V. When sound is being received the voltage rises and falls

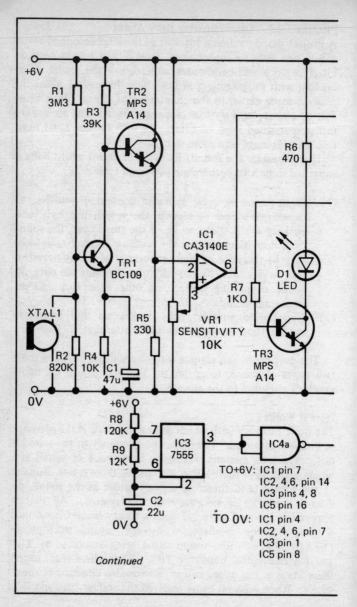

Continued

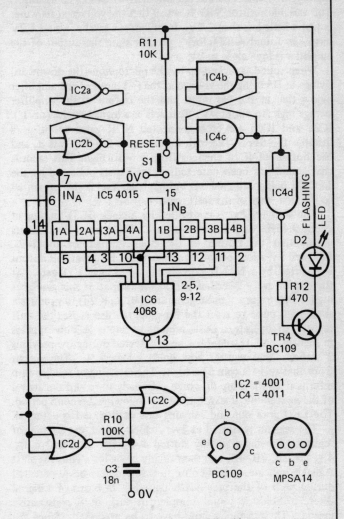

Fig. 88.   *Project 12: Discriminating Baby Alarm.*

rapidly. IC1 is an operational amplifier wired as a comparator. The variable resistor VR1 is set so that the voltage at its wiper is just a little less than 2.5V. In practice, a level of about 1.7V has been found satisfactory. In this state the output of the amplifier is low, close to 0V.

When sound is picked up by the microphone the downward swings at R5 bring the voltage at the (−) input of the amplifier below that at the (+) input and the output of the amplifier swings high, to about 4V. This acts as a logical 'high'. (or '1'). IC2a and IC2b are cross-connected NOR gates acting as a bistable flip-flop. The high input to the flip-flop sets it, and the output of IC2b changes from low to high. This records that sound has been detected, a fact that is indicated by the LED D1 being switched on. A high logic level is also presented to the first stage of the shift register, IC5.

The shift register is controlled by a clock (IC3) running at about 0.45Hz, with a period of 2.2s. The ratio of the resistors means that the output of the clock is high for about 2s, followed by a low period of about 0.2s. However this output is inverted by a NAND gate (IC4a) wired as a NOT gate. At the end of every 2-second period the output of this gate goes high. This triggers a pulse-generator (IC2c, IC2d) to produce a short high pulse to reset the flip-flop. It also causes the shift register to operate. Data present at input A now appears in register 1A. If sound has been detected during the previous 2 seconds, that register now holds a logical '1'. The output from that register (pin 5) is high. The resetting of the flip-flop returns it to the state in which it is ready to record the arrival of the next sound, if any, during the following 2-second period. The LED goes out and remains out until sound is detected.

The register is shifted at every clock period, the content of register 1A being gradually shifted down the chain to 2A, 3A, 4A, 1B, 2B, 3B, 4B, and then finally being lost. Thus the shift register indicates whether or not sound has been detected during each of the previous 8 periods. In terms of a digital filter, it holds a sound sample for each of 8 consecutive periods. These samples now have to be processed. Since the samples are logic levels they can be processed logically. The purpose of the circuit is to discriminate between occasional short-lived sounds and more continuous ones. A series of occasional sounds may cause logical 1's to appear in one or more registers but it is very unlikely that there will be a '1' in *every* register. Indeed, loud sounds occurring 8 times in 16 seconds are very likely to have woken the baby already! We are assuming a rather quieter environment. But if baby is awake and crying or talking to himself or herself continuously for 16 seconds or longer, then all 8 registers will hold '1'. The 8-input NAND gate IC6 detects this event and its output goes low. This sets the second flip-flop (IC4b, IC4c). This being made of NAND gates is set by a low-going pulse, whereas the first flip-flop, made of NOR gates, is set by a high-going pulse.

When the flip-flop is set the output of IC4c goes low. This is inverted by gate IC4d which acts as a buffer to provide base current to TR4. This is turned on and the LED begins to flash. It remains flashing until the flip-flop is reset by pressing the button S1. A flashing LED is used for D2 since this is more eye-catching than a continuously lit LED. D2 can be replaced by an ordinary LED if preferred, but then will need a 470Ω resistor in series with it. If audible warning is required, a low-current audible warning device, preferably with a warbling tone, can be either substituted for D2, or wired in parallel with it. Again, as with input stage, the output is binary. The alarm is either raised or it is not. For this reason there is no need for a D-to-A converter.

This device functions as a low-pass filter. It discriminates between sounds of short duration (a relatively rapid alternation between 'sound' and 'no-sound') and sounds of long duration (a slow alternation). With the NAND gate reading the contents of all 8 registers the filter responds only to sounds lasting 16s or longer. We could say that this is the equivalent of the filter's cut-off point. If you wish the device to respond to sound of shorter duration – to reduce the cut-off point – some of the connections between IC5 and IC6 can be rewired. For example, to give a 10s cut-off point (5 clock stages) remove the connections from the outputs of registers 2B, 3B and 4B. Instead, wire the corresponding inputs of IC6 to the +6V line. The circuit will then respond when the first 5 registers each hold '1'.

Construction

The circuit requires only 20mA when quiescent so it can be operated for considerable periods on a 6V battery. In the long run it is more economical to use a 6V DC mains power supply unit. The circuit consists of only 6 ICs so can be housed in a small plastic case. If it is convenient to place this close by the bed or cot, the microphone may be mounted in the case behind a grille consisting of an array of fine holes drilled in the side of the case. Alternatively, the microphone can be on a lead. The lid or panel of the case carries the sensitivity control (VR1), the indicator LED (D1) and the reset button (S1). The warning devices (D2 or AWD or both) are located in the living room, connected to the main circuit by a pair of light-duty wires.

Build the clock first and check that it runs at the correct rate; it is possible to increase the time-scale of this filter by using a capacitor of larger value for C2. Next build the amplifier and comparator section, together with the pulse-generator and flip-flop (IC2a–d). Also connect Gate a of IC4. While testing at this stage connect the unused inputs of IC4 to the 0V or +6V lines. To check the circuit measure the voltage at pin 2 of IC1, then set the sensitivity adjustment to bring the voltage at pin 3 about 0.5V lower than this. The output at pin 6 is low and, at the next clock pulse, the flip-flop is reset and D1 goes out. Any small noise made near the microphone sets the flip-flop and D1 comes on. It goes out again at the next clock pulse.

Now add the shift register, IC5 and the 8-input NAND gate. As mentioned earlier, it is not necessary to connect all 8 registers to the gate, but all inputs to IC6 must be connected to something, either to IC5 or to the +6V rail. If you wish to allow the discrimination period of the filter to be variable, a rotary switch could be included here to allow different numbers of registers to be connected to IC6. Testing at this stage shows that the output of IC6 (pin 13) is normally high and stays high in the absence of sound. If you make a sound each time the flip-flop resets (i.e. each time D1 goes out) then D1 comes on again each time and the output of IC6 goes low after 8 such noises. But if you make a sound only occasionally, not after each of 8 consecutive clock pulses, the output of IC6 stays high.

Complete the circuit by building the NAND flip-flop of IC4, and wiring its output through IC4d to TR4. Add the flashing LED and possibly an audible warning device.

To use the alarm, first set the sensitivity control (VR1) so that D1 comes on whenever a sound of sufficient loudness is made. If the bedroom is by a noisy road or there are other frequent sources of sound, it may be necessary to position the microphone closer to the cot or bed and to reduce the sensitivity. Making as little noise as possible, press the reset button and hold it for 2–3 seconds until D1 goes out. D2 then stops flashing. If you make a sound when leaving the room or closing the door, this will not normally matter because the filter rejects it as a short-period sound.

Special Components

XTAL1 is a cheap crystal microphone; a 'microphone insert' is very suitable.

VR1 is a panel-mounting 'volume control' carbon potentiometer, complete with a knob.

D1 is an ordinary LED, but D2 is preferably one with built-in flashing circuit. If audible warning is required, use a solid-state audible warning device or electronic 'buzzer' suited to operating on 6V.

The ICs are as follows:

IC1	CA30140E CMOS operational amplifier
IC2	4001 CMOS quadruple 2-input NOR gate
IC3	7555 CMOS timer
IC4	4011 CMOS quadruple 2-input NAND gate
IC5	4015 CMOS dual 4-stage shift register (serial-in parallel-out)
IC6	4068 CMOS 8-input NAND gate.

Chapter 11

PRACTICAL FILTER DESIGNS

This chapter is a summary of simple filter circuits, most of which have already been described earlier in the book. It is intended as a guide to designing filters for use in conjunction with some of the projects in this book, or with other circuits.

The precision of a filter depends mainly on the precision of the resistors and capacitors used in its construction. Often the capacitors are the limiting factor because it is not easy to obtain high-tolerance capacitors in a wide range of values. The precision of the filter is determined by the tolerance of the *least* precise component, so there is no point in using 1% tolerance resistors if the capacitors are only 10% tolerance.

Choosing Capacitors

1 Silvered mica capacitors have the highest tolerance (±1%, except for the very smallest values) but the maximum value commonly available is only 4.7nF. They have good temperature stability too, another factor to be taken into account if the circuit is to operate over a wide temperature range.

2 Close tolerance polystyrene capacitors (±1%) are available in capacitances up to 22nF, and also have good temperature stability. They are very suitable for filters.

3 Ceramic capacitors are of 3 main types. Metallised ceramic plate capacitors have good tolerance (±2%) and temperature stability in values up to about 330pF. Resin-dipped ceramics have reasonable tolerance (±5% up to 220pF). They are also available in values up to 470nF but with lower tolerance (±10% or ±20%). Disc ceramics have very poor tolerance, −20% to +80% making them quite unsuited to filtering circuits.

4 Polyester capacitors are the most sensible choice when a capacitor of larger value is required. They are manufactured in a full range of values up to about 2.2µF. Their tolerance is relatively low (±5% or ±10%) and their temperature stability is poor, but they are adequate for very many filtering purposes. Generally the *polyester layer* type is to be preferred and, with these, the higher values have better tolerance than the lower values.

5 Electrolytic capacitors have a tolerance of ±20% or worse and their capacity is subject to change with age and with the degree of use. This and the fact that they are polarised makes electrolytic capacitors unsuitable for use in filters. However, a limited range of non-polarised electrolytic capacitors is available, intended for use in loudspeaker cross-over networks and these can be used in filters where high capacitance ($1.5\mu F$ to $100\mu F$) is essential and low precision is acceptable.

6 Tantalum capacitors are unsuitable for the same reasons as electrolytic capacitors.

Designing Filters A: Passive RC Filters

These are the easiest and cheapest to build, but suffer from the disadvantages of low input impedance, high output impedance, reduction in signal amplitude and low Q. The resistor and capacitor values shown in Figure 89 are for a low-pass or a high-pass filter with cut-off at 1kHz. This is based on the equation:

$$f_c = 1/2\pi RC$$

Since the factor $1/2\pi$ comes into the equations of almost all filters, it is convenient to replace it in the equation with its numerical equivalent:

$$f_c = 0.16/RC$$

This equation applies to many types of filter. Although the value of the dividend in the equation above works out more precisely to 0.1592, the given value 0.16 is correct within ±1%, which is close enough for most practical purposes.

The roll-off in the stop-band is −6dB per octave for the first-order low-pass filter and +6dB per octave for the first-

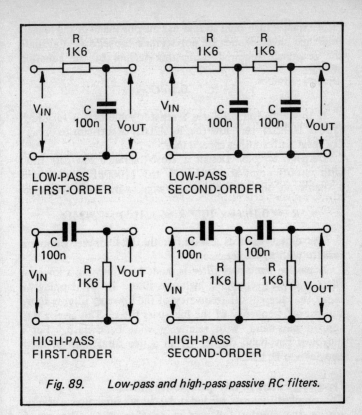

LOW-PASS
FIRST-ORDER

LOW-PASS
SECOND-ORDER

HIGH-PASS
FIRST-ORDER

HIGH-PASS
SECOND-ORDER

Fig. 89.   Low-pass and high-pass passive RC filters.

order high-pass filter. The second-order filters have roll-offs of $-12dB$ and $+12dB$ per octave respectively.

The phase lag ϕ of a first-order low-pass filter is $-45°$ at the cut-off frequency F_c, less (approaching $0°$) at lower frequencies and more (approaching $-90°$) at higher frequencies. For a second-order low-pass filter, $\phi = -90°$ at f_c, less at lower frequencies and more (approaching $-180°$) at higher frequencies. For the high-pass filters the phase lead at f_c is the same as the lag for low-pass filters, but increases with lower frequencies and decreases with higher frequencies.

Design procedure: Decide on a capacitor value, one that is easily obtainable; usually it is preferable to pick a lower value rather than a high one, so that use may be made of the higher-tolerance silvered mica or polystyrene capacitors. Calculate the resistance required using this version of the equation above:

$$R = 0.16/Cf_c$$

If this equation produces a resistor value that is very high (above 100kΩ), very low (below 470Ω) or difficult to obtain, try again with another capacitance.

Design example: Design a close-tolerance low-pass filter with cut-off point at 66kHz. A 1nF (1000pF) capacitor is available in the silvered mica range, with ±1% tolerance.

$$R = 0.16/(1 \times 10^{-9} \times 66 \times 10^3) = 2424\Omega$$

The cloest value is 2.4kΩ, in the E24 range. Choose a resistor with ±1% tolerance.

A passive *band-pass filter* is made by following a low-pass filter with an overlapping high-pass filter. By overlapping we mean that the cut-off frequency of the low-pass filter is *above* the cut-off frequency of the high-pass filter. This gives a flat-topped pass-band, with relatively wide bandwidth. For a narrower pass-band (higher Q) an active filter must be used. See Section D, below.

Designing Filters B: Low-pass Active Filters

The simplest low-pass second-order active filter uses a transistor in the emitter follower mode (Fig. 90). The cut-off frequency is given by $0.16/RC$, as above, where R1 = R2 and C1 = C2. The component values in the figure are for f_c = 1kHz. For other frequencies, calculate values as in the design example above. Roll-off in the stop band for this and the other second-order filters is −12dB per octave. Phase-change is −90° at f_c, ranging from 0° to −180° for lower and higher frequencies respectively.

The low-pass second-order filter based on an operational amplifier has the same features but with the ability to control damping (and hence Q) more precisely. This allows us to design filters with a particular response, such as Butterworth, Bessel and Chebyshev (page 51). With R1 = R2 and C1 = C2,

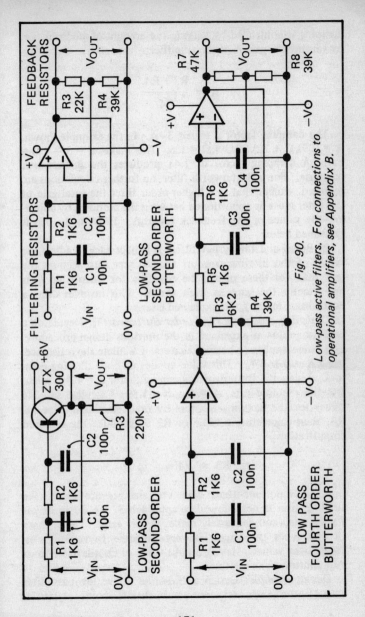

Fig. 90.

Low-pass active filters. For connections to operational amplifiers, see Appendix B.

damping is controlled by varying the amount of feedback, i.e. by varying the gain A of the amplifier:

$$A = \frac{R3 + R4}{R4}$$

The damping factor d equals 3—A. In the example shown, A = (39kΩ + 22kΩ)/39kΩ = 1.6. This makes d = 3 − 1.6 = 1.4. A damping factor of 1.41 produces the *Butterworth* response. For a Butterworth filter, no further calculations are required, except that in a higher-order filter the total gain of the filter must be apportioned between the sections, by adjusting the values of the feedback resistors. How to do this is explained below.

In Bessel and Chebyshev filters it is necessary to adjust the values of the filtering resistors too, to take into account the fact that, for these filters, the equation for calculating f_c is not exactly the same as given above. This involves using a normalising factor f_n, as explained later.

Designing procedure (2nd-order Butterworth): Decide on a capacitor value as explained in the previous design procedure. This value applies to both capacitors. Calculate the resistance, using $R = 0.16/Cf_c$. This value applies to both filtering resistors. Using the Butterworth damping factor d = 1.41, calculate the required gain, A = 3 − d = 1.59. Calculate suitable values for the damping resistors by first selecting a value for R4, then calculating a value of R3 to produce the required amplification:

$$R3 = R4(A - 1)$$

It is important that, whatever changes are made, the amplification is not allowed to approach 3. To do so makes d very small and conversely makes Q very large. Under these circumstances the circuit is very sensitive to variations in component values. Having a large value of Q, it is liable to go into continuous oscillation.

Design example: Design a 2nd-order active low-pass filter with Butterworth response and cut-off point at 50Hz.

Obviously a fairly large capacitance is required. As a first trial, 220nF capacitors would require resistors of $R = 0.16/(220 \times 10^{-9} \times 50) = 14.5\text{k}\Omega$. Polyester layer capacitors of 220nF have ±5% tolerance, so 15kΩ resistors would be close enough. The Butterworth damping factor is $d = 1.41$. Therefore A = 3 − 1.41 = 1.59. Decide on 39kΩ for R4, then R3 = R4 (1.59 − 1) = R4 × 0.59 = 39kΩ × 0.59 = 23.01kΩ. A 24kΩ is the nearest E24 value, but the more readily available 22kΩ resistor could equally well be used when only ±5% tolerance is provided by the capacitor.

Design procedure (2nd-order Bessel): Decide on a capacitor value as explained in the previous design procedure. This value applies to both capacitors. Calculate the resistance, using $R = 0.16/Cf_c$. Then divide this by the normalising factor, $f_n = 1.27$. This value applies to both filtering resistors.

Using the Bessel damping factor $d = 1.73$, calculate the required gain, A = 3 − d = 1.27. Calculate suitable values for the damping resistors by first selecting a value for R4, then calculating a value of R3 to produce the required amplification:

$$R3 = R4(A - 1)$$

Incidentally, the fact that A equals 1.27, the same value as the normalising factor, is coincidental and applies only to the second-order Bessel filter. In other filters the two factors have different values, as will be seen in later paragraphs.

Design example: Design a 2nd-order active low-pass filter with Bessel response and cut-off point at 800Hz. 10nF capacitors would require resistors of $R = 0.16/(10 \times 10^{-9} \times 800) = 20\text{k}\Omega$. Divide by the normalising factor: 20kΩ/1.27 = 15.7kΩ. A 16kΩ resistor gives precision between +1% and +3%. High-precision (±1%) polystyrene capacitors are available for 10nF (10,000pF), so a high-precision filter could be built by using a 15.8kΩ resistor from the E96 range.

The damping factor is 1.73, so A = 1.27. Decide on 39kΩ for R4, then R3 = R4(1.27 − 1) = R4 × 0.27 = 39kΩ × 0.27 = 10.5kΩ. The nearest standard values are 10kΩ and 11kΩ, but give only ±5% precision. If ±1% precision is essential then use the 10.5kΩ value from the E96 range.

Design procedure (2nd-order Chebyshev): We confine this description to the Chebyshev filter with 2dB ripples in the pass-band. Decide on a capacitor value as explained in the previous design procedure. This value applies to both capacitors. Calculate the resistance, using $R = 0.16/Cf_c$. Then divide this by the normalising factor, $f_n = 0.91$. This value applies to both filtering resistors.

Using the Chebyshev damping factor $d = 0.89$, calculate the required gain, $A = 3 - d = 2.11$. Calculate suitable values for the damping resistors by first selecting a value for R4, then calculating a value of R3 to produce the required amplification:

$$R3 = R4(A - 1)$$

Design example: Design a 2nd-order active low-pass filter with the 2dB ripples Chebyshev response and cut-off point at 100kHz. 100pF capacitors would require a resistor of $R = 0.16/(100 \times 10^{-12} \times 100 \times 10^3) = 16k\Omega$. Divide by the normalising factor: $16k\Omega/0.91 = 17.6k\Omega$. An 18k$\Omega$ resistor is the nearest standard value.

The damping factor is 0.89, so $A = 2.11$. Decide on 39kΩ for R4, then $R3 = R4(2.11 - 1) = R4 \times 1.11 = 39k\Omega \times 1.11 = 43.3k\Omega$. The nearest standard value is 43kΩ.

Design procedure (4th-order Butterworth): The values shown in Figure 90 for the fourth-order filter give a Butterworth response. The cut-off frequency is calculated from the usual equation, in which $R = R1 = R2 = R5 = R6$, and $C = C1 = C2 = C3 = C4$. Decide on a capacitor value as explained in the previous design procedure. This value applies to all 4 capacitors. Calculate the resistance, using $R = 0.16/Cf_c$. This value applies to all 4 filtering resistors.

The damping factor d is 1.848 for the first section and 0.765 for the second section. This gives gains of 1.152 and 2.235 respectively, giving an overall gain of $1.152 \times 2.235 = 2.6$ for the whole filter. Calculate R3 and R4 to obtain a gain of 1.152, and R8 and R8 to obtain a gain of 2.235:

$$R3 = R4(A_1 - 1) = R4 \times 0.152$$
$$R7 = R8(A_2 - 1) = R8 \times 2.235$$

174

Design example: Design a 4th-order active low-pass filter with Butterworth response and cut-off point at 5kHz. Select 10nF as the capacitor value for both sections. $R = 0.16/(10 \times 10^{-9} \times 5 \times 10^3) = 3.2\text{k}\Omega$. Use an E12 resistor of 3.3kΩ, or a precision E96 resistor of 3.16kΩ or 3.24kΩ. In the damping equations, assume that R4 = R8 = 39kΩ. Then calculate R3 = 39k$\Omega \times 0.152 = 5.9k\Omega$. Calculate R7 = 39k$\Omega \times 1.235 = 48.2k\Omega$. 5.6k$\Omega$ and 47kΩ resistors would be close enough for a low-precision filter.

Design procedure (4th-order Bessel): Decide on a capacitor. This value applies to all 4 capacitors. Calculate the resistance, using $R = 0.16/Cf_c$. Then divide this resistance by the normalisation factors, which are 1.43 for the first section and 1.61 for the second section. Thus R1 = R2 = $R/1.43$, and R5 = R6 = $R/1.61$.

The damping factor d is 1.916 for the first section and 1.241 for the second section. This gives gains of 1.084 and 1.759 respectively, giving an overall gain of 1.084 $\times$ 1.759 = 1.9 for the whole filter. Calculate R3 and R4 to obtain a gain of 1.084, and R7 and R8 to obtain a gain of 1.759:

$$R3 = R4(A_1 - 1) = R4 \times 0.084$$
$$R7 = R8(A_2 - 1) = R8 \times 0.759$$

Design example: Design a 4th-order active low-pass filter with Bessel response and cut-off point at 120kHz. Try 1nF as the capacitor value for both sections. $R = 0.16/1 \times 10^{-9} \times 120 \times 10^3) = 1.333k\Omega$. For the first section R1 = R2 = 1.333k$\Omega/1.43 = 932\Omega$. For the second section, R5 = R6 = 1.333k$\Omega/1.61 = 828\Omega$. Use the nearest values 910Ω and 820Ω.

In the damping equations, assume that R4 = R8 = 39kΩ. Then calculate R3 = 39k$\Omega \times 0.084 = 3.3k\Omega$. Calculate R7 = 39k$\Omega \times 0.759 = 29.6k\Omega$. 3.3k$\Omega$ and 30kΩ resistors will be satisfactory.

Design procedure (4th-order Chebyshev): This is the 2dB ripple version. Decide on a capacitor value. This value applies to all 4 capacitors. Calculate the resistance, using $R = 0.16/Cf_c$. Then divide this resistance by the normalisation factors, which are 0.47 for the first section and 0.96 for the second

175

section. Thus R1 = R2 = $R/0.47$, and R5 = R6 = $R/0.96$.

The damping factor d is 1.076 for the first section and 0.218 for the second section. This gives gains of 1.924 and 2.782 respectively, giving an overall gain of 1.924 × 2.782 = 5.4 for the whole filter. Calculate R3 and R4 to obtain a gain of 1.924, and R7 and R8 to obtain a gain of 2.782:

$$R3 = R4(A_1 - 1) = R4 \times 0.924$$
$$R7 = R8(A_2 - 1) = R8 \times 1.782$$

Design example: Design a 4th-order active low-pass filter with Chebyshev 2dB ripple response and cut-off point at 100Hz. Try 100nF as the capacitor value for both sections. $R = 0.16/(100 \times 10^{-9} \times 100) = 16\text{k}\Omega$. For the first section R1 = R2 = $16\text{k}\Omega/0.47 = 34\text{k}\Omega$. For the second section, R5 = R6 = $16\text{k}\Omega/1.61 = 9.9\text{k}\Omega$. Use the nearest values 33kΩ and 10kΩ.

In the damping equations, assume that R4 = R8 = 39kΩ. Then calculate R3 = 39kΩ × 0.924 = 36.0kΩ. Calculate R7 = 39kΩ × 1.782 = 69.5kΩ. 36kΩ and 68kΩ resistors will be satisfactory.

Designing filters with steeper cut-off: The second-order active low-pass filters have a roll-off of −12dB per octave, and the fourth-order filters have a roll-of of −24dB per octave. If steeper roll-off is required, precede the filter with one or more passive sections, with cut-off of the same frequency. For example, preceding a fourth-order active filter with a second-order passive filter increases the roll-off to −36dB per octave. This addition affects the damping of the filter as a whole and it is necessary to adjust the values of the feedback resistors in the active sections if a filter with a particular response is to be built. The simplest way of tackling this is to breadboard the feedback parts of the filter and experiment with various resistor values. In general terms, it will be necessary to reduce damping to compensate for the damping inherent in the passive filters. Try reducing the values of R3 and R7.

Designing Filters C: High-pass Active Filters

Circuits for high-pass active filters are the same as those in Figure 90 except that the filtering resistors (R1, R2, R5, R6) are exchanged with the capacitors (C1, C2, C3, C4). The response of the filter at the highest frequencies in its pass-band are limited by the frequency response of the operational amplifier (page 60).

Design procedures: The procedures are exactly the same as those for the corresponding low-pass filters except that we *multiply* by the normalisation factor instead of dividing by it.

Design example: Design a 2nd order active high-pass filter with Bessel response and cut-off point at 800Hz (compare page 173). 10nF capacitors require resistors of $0.16/(10 \times 10^9 \times 800) = 20\text{k}\Omega$. Multiply by the normalising factor: $20\text{k}\Omega \times 1.27 = 25.4\text{k}\Omega$. A 24kΩ resistor gives reasonable precision, although with high-precision polyester capacitors it is more appropriate to use the 25.5kΩ resistor from the E96 range. The rest of the design is as on page 173.

Designing Filters D: Band-pass Active Filters

For a broad, flat-topped pass band, with fractional bandwidth greater than about 1 (see page 75) use a low-pass filter and feed its output to a high-pass filter. For a narrower pass band use a multiple feedback filter (Fig. 91).

Design procedure: Given the lower and upper −3dB points, f_L and f_H, calculate the bandwidth, $\Delta f = f_H - f_L$. Then calculate the centre frequency f_0:

$$f_0 = \sqrt{(f_L \times f_H)}$$

Finally calculate the fractional bandwidth $= \Delta f/f_0$. If, instead of the above parameters, we are given the centre frequency f_0 and Q, we calculate the fractional bandwidth from $1/Q$.

From this point the procedure takes one of two directions:

(1) If the fractional bandwidth is greater than 1 (or thereabouts) design a low-pass filter with cut-off frequency f_H (note the suffix!), and a high-pass filter with cut-off frequency f_L. Feed the signal to the low-pass filter and

177

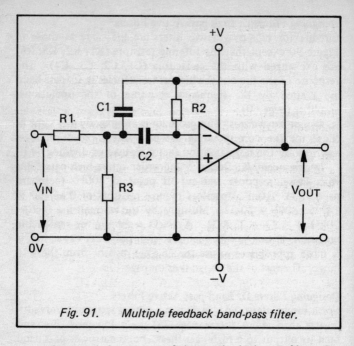

Fig. 91. Multiple feedback band-pass filter.

then send the output of this to the high-pass filter. See pages 168–177 for further details.

(2) If the fractional bandwidth is less than 1 (high Q), design a multiple feedback filter, as follows. First decide on the voltage gain A at the centre frequency, f_0. This could be 1, or possibly more. Next decide on a suitable value C for the capacitors, taking into account the fact that precision is particularly important in band-pass circuits.

Calculate the value of resistor R1:

$$R1 = 0.159/(\Delta f \times A \times C)$$

Calculate the value of resistor R2:

$$R2 = 0.318/(\Delta f \times C)$$

Calculate the value of resistor R3:

$$R3 = \frac{R1}{(39.5 \times f_0{}^2 \times C^2 \times R1 \times R2) - 1}$$

Note that the only expression involving f_0 is the last one, indicating that, given fixed values for the capacitors and for resistors R1 and R2, the centre frequency can be set by varying only R3. R3 can be replaced by a variable resistor, giving a tunable band-pass filter. Tuning has no effect on the bandwidth or gain.

Design example: Design a band-pass filter, bandwidth Δf = 100Hz, centre frequency f_0 = 1kHz, gain A = 5. The fractional bandwidth is $1000/100$ = 10, so this is a filter that requires a multiple feedback circuit.

The capacitor value is selected as 10nF.

$R1 = 0.159/(100 \times 5 \times 10 \times 10^{-9}) = 31.8\text{k}\Omega$

$R2 = 0.318/(100 \times 10 \times 10^{-9}) = 318\text{k}\Omega$

$R3 =$
$$\frac{31.8 \times 10^3}{(39.5 \times 1000^2 \times 100 \times 10^{-18} \times 31.8 \times 10^3 \times 318 \times 10^3) - 1}$$

$= 817\Omega.$

Suitable values are $33\text{k}\Omega$, $330\text{k}\Omega$, and 820Ω, but closer tolerance for the first two of these would be preferred.

Design procedure (4th-order band-pass filter): If a slightly wider pass band is required, combined with steep roll-off on either side, cascade two multiple feedback filters, with staggered frequencies. The Q for both filters is identical. If f_0 is the required central frequency, decide on a staggering factor a and design the filters as above with the central frequency of one being (f_0/a) while the central frequency of the other is $(f_0 \times a)$. The larger the value of a, the flatter the top until, with increasing a, a slight dip appears at f_0. In general, the value of a should range between 1.005 and 2.0.

Designing Filters E: Notch Filters

One method of obtaining a notch filter is to sum the low-pass and high-pass outputs of a state-variable filter. This is described on page 94. The circuit in Figure 92 shows a notch filter that can be built as a fixed-frequency filter or as a tunable filter. This is an improvement on the twin-T filter of Figure 46 which has low Q.

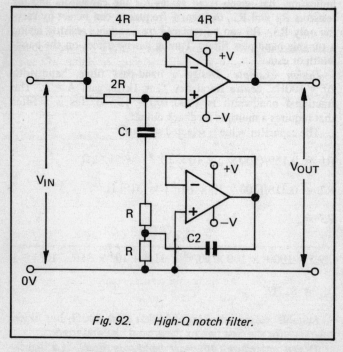

Fig. 92.   High-Q notch filter.

Design procedure (high-Q notch filter): The easiest method is for the resistors to have the ratios shown in Figure 92. C1 should have a value in the range 100pF to 39nF, while C2 should be in the range 100nF to 10μF. Thus C2 is 200–1000 times C1. Decide on suitable values of C1 and C2, bearing in mind that component tolerance is extremely important in resonant filters such as this. As a starting point, a suitable pair of values is C1 = 2.2nF and C2 = 1μF. Then calculate *R* from the equation:

$$R = \frac{0.16}{f_0\sqrt{(C1 \times C2)}}$$

Stray capacitance in the circuit as well as other factors may affect the centre frequency, especially at frequencies of several hundred hertz or more. In this case, centre frequency can be corrected by altering the resistors labelled 'R'. Increase one of them and decrease the other, keeping the *total* of these resistors equal to 2R. A simple way of doing this is to replace the 'R' resistors with a variable resistor of value 2R as in Figure 93.

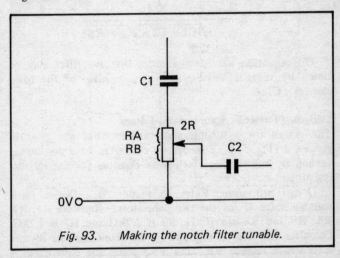

Fig. 93.   Making the notch filter tunable.

The Q of this filter, when the 'R' resistors are equal is:

$$Q = \frac{1}{2}\sqrt{\frac{C2}{C1}}$$

When using this circuit it is usually necessary to limit the amplitude of the input signal. Otherwise the amplifiers become saturated and the output signal is badly distorted.

Design example: Design a notch filter with centre frequency 100Hz. Start with C1 = 2.2nF and C2 = 1μF. Calculate $\sqrt{(C1 \times C2)} = \sqrt{(2.2 \times 10^{-9} \times 1 \times 10^{-6})} = 4.69 \times 10^{-8}$. Then $R = 0.16/(100 \times 4.69 \times 10^{-8}) = 34k\Omega$. Use 33k$\Omega$, 68k$\Omega$ and 130kΩ resistors for R, $2R$ and $4R$ respectively. For highest precision use 34kΩ, 68kΩ and 137kΩ from the E96 range. The Q of this filter is 10.7.

Substituting a variable resistor as in Figure 91 not only provides a means of trimming the centre frequency but also makes the filter tunable. If the resistances of the two portions of the resistor are R_A and R_B, as in the figure, the centre frequency is:

$$f_0 = \frac{0.16}{\sqrt{(C1 \times C2 \times R_A \times R_B)}}$$

This equation also demonstrates that the filter may be tuned by using a variable capacitor in place of the fixed capacitor C1.

Designing Filters F: State-variable Filters

The circuit for a tunable state-variable filter was given in Project 4 (Fig. 51). This can be converted to a non-tuning version by substituting fixed-value resistors for the variable resistors.

Design procedure: Refer to Figure 51. Decide on a suitable value C for the two capacitors. Resistors R1, R2, R4, R5 and R8 are 10kΩ, R3 is 2.7kΩ and R7 is 4.7kΩ. Calculate the value R required for the fixed resistors R9 and R10 which replace VR2 and VR3 using the equation $R = 0.16/Cf_0$. Given the required value of Q, calculate the value of R6 using the equation R6 = 10kΩ $\times$ Q. Given the required gain A, calculate the value of the fixed resistor R11 to replace VR1 using the equation R11 = R6/A. If variable gain or Q are required, VR1 and VR4 can be left as in Figure 51.

Design example: Design a state-variable filter with f_0 = 400Hz, Q = 3 and A = 2. A suitable value for C1 and C2 is 100nF. $R = 0.16/(100 \times 10^{-9} \times 400) = 4k\Omega$. Since Q is to be reasonably low, then 3.9kΩ resistors can be used for

R9 and R10. R6 = $10k\Omega \times 3 = 30k\Omega$. R11 = $30k\Omega/2 = 15k\Omega$. The other resistors are as listed in the design procedure.

Appendix A

FURTHER READING

The following books, published by Bernard Babani (publishing) Ltd and all written by R. A. Penfold, will help the beginner to build the projects in this book:

227, *Beginners Guide to Building Electronic Projects*

BP48, *Electronic Projects for Beginners*

BP110, *How to Get Your Electronic Projects Working*

BP121, *How to Design and Make Your Own PCBs*

For a more mathematically detailed account of active filters, including 'recipes' for a wide range of practical filter circuits, refer to:

Don Lancaster, *Active-Filter Cookbook*, Howard W. Sams and Company, ISBN 0 672 21168 8.

Appendix B

PIN-OUTS OF ICs

Figure 94 shows the terminal connections of the quadruple logic gate ICs used in this book as seen from above. Although the figure shows the NAND gates of the 4011 IC, the same arrangement is found for the NOR gates of the 4001. Most single op amp ICs have the pin-out shown in Figure 95. These include the 741, LF351, LF355, CA3130E and CA3140E. Pins 1, 5 and 8 are for off-set nulling in ways that differ from one type to another. We do not use these terminals in this book. Figure 96 shows the LF347 quadruple JFET op amp used in several projects.

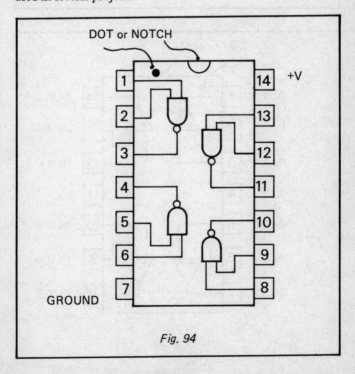

Fig. 94

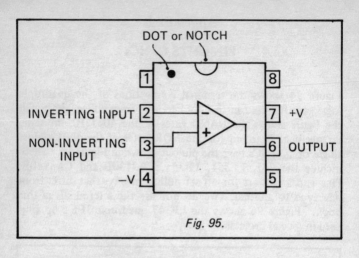

Fig. 95.

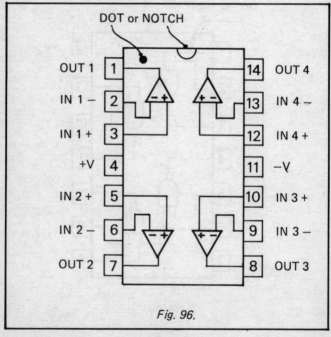

Fig. 96.

Notes

Notes

Notes